D1373879

Topics in Modern Mathematics

contributing authors

University of Waterloo

G. BERMAN
K. D. FRYER
J. W. GRAHAM
D. A. SPROTT
R. G. STANTON
D. G. WERTHEIM

Topics in Modern Mathematics

edited by

RALPH G. STANTON
KENNETH D. FRYER

Department of Mathematics
University of Waterloo

PRENTICE-HALL, INC.
Englewood Cliffs, N.J.

PRENTICE-HALL MATHEMATICS SERIES
Albert A. Bennett, Editor

PRENTICE-HALL INTERNATIONAL, INC., LONDON
PRENTICE-HALL OF AUSTRALIA, PTY., LTD., SYDNEY
PRENTICE-HALL OF CANADA, LTD., TORONTO
PRENTICE-HALL OF INDIA (PRIVATE) LTD., NEW DELHI
PRENTICE-HALL OF JAPAN, INC., TOKYO

Third printing..... ...September, 1965

Library of Congress Catalog No. 63–20959
Printed in the United States of America

C 92560

Preface

In the past few years, a great deal of publicity has been accorded to the rather vague subject of "modern mathematics". Teachers and students at the secondary level and the junior college level have become increasingly interested in finding out just what meaning is attached to some of the terms such as fields, matrices, truth tables, et cetera, which are being used in some of the educational literature. The present volume grew out of an attempt to answer questions on topics such as these.

In the Autumn of 1959, the Department of Mathematics of the University of Waterloo sponsored a series of seminars on "aspects of modern mathematics". These were widely attended by secondary school teachers, and a subsequent publication of the lectures in mimeographed form was well received. The lectures have now been considerably revised and amplified, and are published with the hope that teachers who are interested in relatively simple and self-contained accounts of the topics covered will find them of use. Certainly, the original group of teachers did find it useful to have a reference where material on these topics was collected in one volume.

By design, there has been considerable variety in the range of topics covered and in the level of presentation. Several of the topics are, by nature, more difficult than others (for example, Statistics). Consequently, there is material which can be of interest to a wide variety of teachers, both those whose mathematical training is somewhat limited and those who possess a more extensive background.

It should be emphasized that an attempt has been made to maintain some of the informality used in the original lecture presentation; the chapters are meant to provide discussion of various topics.

The main responsibility for writing and presentation of the various chapters is as follows:

Chapter 1	—Groups and Fields	R. G. Stanton
Chapter 2	—Set Theory	K. D. Fryer
Chapter 3	—Boolean Algebra	G. Berman
Chapter 4	—Logic and Computing	R. G. Stanton
Chapter 5	—Vector Spaces and Matrices	K. D. Fryer
Chapter 6	—Numerical Analysis	J. W. Graham
Chapter 7	—Functions of a Single Variable	R. G. Stanton
Chapter 8	—Fundamental Concepts of Calculus	D. G. Wertheim
Chapter 9	—Probability Theory and Statistics	D. A. Sprott
Chapter 10	—Some Types of Geometry	G. Berman
Epilogue	—Some Questions about Modern Mathematics in the Secondary School Curriculum	R. G. Stanton and K. D. Fryer

The various chapters present relevant material in a manner which attempts to be factual and mathematical. The controversial question of whether the material presented is all appropriate for presentation at an elementary level is raised in the Epilogue. The views suggested in this epilogue are naturally subjective. However, in view of the great amount of publicity which has been accorded the ideas of presenting "progressive" mathematics in the secondary schools, it is hoped that it will be serviceable to present a few remarks favouring a more traditional and conservative point of view. The authors are quite in agreement that the material contained in this volume, together with much other material, is appropriate knowledge for secondary school teachers; but they feel it is a legitimate matter for discussion as to whether all such material should be presented to secondary school students. The questions raised in the Epilogue probably have no unique answers; but it is hoped that they may stimulate discussion and open-minded investigation of controversial issues.

The authors would like to express their keen appreciation to Mrs. A. J. Fielding who typed the various versions of the manuscript and to Mr. Peter J. Ponzo of the University of Illinois, who made the diagrams.

Contents

Topics in Modern Mathematics

I

Groups and Fields

by Ralph G. Stanton

1.1. ALGEBRAIC STRUCTURES

The basic concept of modern algebra is that of an *algebraic structure*; this concept, which will be exemplified in the present chapter, allows us to treat many apparently diverse topics as special cases of one general idea. Such a procedure leads to greater coherence and unity.

In any algebraic structure, comprising elements $a, b, c, \ldots$, we shall want an *equivalence relation* which we call R. An equivalence relation is defined to be a relation R between elements which obeys the following rules (the double arrow $\Rightarrow$ is used as an abbreviation for "imply" or "implies").

(1.1.1) *The Reflexive Law:* aRa, that is, the element a is related to a.

(1.1.2) *The Symmetric Law:* $aRb \Rightarrow bRa$, that is, if a is related to b, then this implies that b is related to a.

(1.1.3) *The Transitive Law:* $aRb, bRc \Rightarrow aRc$, that is, if a is related to b and b is related to c, then this implies that a is related to c.

Simple examples of equivalence relations are the ordinary equality relation, denoted by the symbol $=$, which relates the elements of the real number system; and the congruence relation, denoted by the symbol $\equiv$, which relates geometric figures when subjected to rigid motion in plane Euclidean geometry.

Example 1.1.1. Check that the relation R "to have the same parents as" is an equivalence relation among human beings $a, b, c, \ldots$.

aRa: a has the same parents as a.

$aRb \Rightarrow bRa$: if a has the same parents as b, this implies that b has the same parents as a.

$aRb, bRc \Rightarrow aRc$: if a has the same parents as b, and b has the same parents as c, then a has the same parents as c.

Example 1.1.2. Consider the real number system and define a triplet ratio to be a set of three real numbers written $(a : b : c)$. Equivalence of triplet ratios is denoted by the sign $::$, and we define

$$(a : b : c) :: (a_1 : b_1 : c_1) \tag{1.1.4}$$

[read as: $(a : b : c)$ is equivalent to $(a_1 : b_1 : c_1)$] if and only if there exists a constant $k \neq 0$ such that

$$a = ka_1, \qquad b = kb_1, \qquad c = kc_1. \tag{1.1.5}$$

Show that $::$ is an equivalence relation.

Clearly $(a : b : c) :: (a : b : c)$, by taking $k = 1$.

Also, if $(a : b : c) :: (a_1 : b_1 : c_1)$, we can write [using (1.1.5)]

$$a_1 = k^{-1}a, \qquad b_1 = k^{-1}b, \qquad c_1 = k^{-1}c,$$

that is,

$$(a_1 : b_1 : c_1) :: (a : b : c).$$

Finally, if

$$(a : b : c) :: (a_1 : b_1 : c_1) \quad \text{and} \quad (a_1 : b_1 : c_1) :: (a_2 : b_2 : c_2),$$

then

$$a = ka_1, \quad b = kb_1, \quad c = kc_1; \qquad a_1 = k_1a_2, \quad b_1 = k_1b_2, \quad c_1 = k_1c_2.$$

Hence

$$a = (kk_1)a_2, \qquad b = (kk_1)b_2, \qquad c = (kk_1)c_2.$$

Thus we have verified the reflexive, symmetric, and transitive laws for the relation $::$; hence $::$ is an equivalence relation.

EXERCISES

1. Which of the following are equivalence relations?
   (a) Similarity of geometric figures.
   (b) Being a friend of.

(c) Having the same first letter as (a relation between words).

(d) The inequality relation $\neq$ (between real numbers).

(e) The "less-than" relation $<$ (between real numbers).

(f) The greater-than-or-equal-to relation $\geq$ (between real numbers).

(g) Being a brother of.

(h) Being a sib (sister or brother) of.

2. In Exercise 1, point out which of the three laws are satisfied by the various relations described.

3. In analogy to Example 1.1.2, define and discuss doublet ratios $(a:b)$ of real numbers. Why is a doublet ratio $(a:b)$ more general than a fraction a/b?

1.2. FIELDS

One of the most familiar algebraic structures is a field. In talking about fields, we shall make use of the term *binary operation* to refer to an operation which produces a third element from *two* given elements; these two given elements are not necessarily distinct. Also we shall use the symbol ϵ as an abbreviation for "is an element of". We then define a field as follows.

A *field* F is a set of elements $a, b, c, \ldots,$ with two binary operations $+$ and $\times$, which obeys the following axioms.

(1.2.1) (a) $a + b \in F$ (*closure under addition*; that is, the operation $+$ produces from every pair of elements a and b in F a third element, called $a + b$, which is also in F);

(b) $(a + b) + c = a + (b + c)$ (*associative addition*; that is, parentheses may be introduced anywhere in a sum);

(c) $a + b = b + a$ (*commutative addition*; that is, the order in which field elements are added is immaterial);

(d) there exists an element 0 (zero) such that $a + 0 = a$ (zero is called the *additive identity*);

(e) there exists, for every element a in F, an element called $(-a)$ in F such that $a + (-a) = 0$ (this element $-a$ is called the *additive inverse* of a).

(1.2.2) (a) $ab \in F$ (*closure under multiplication*; that is, the operation $\times$ produces from every pair of elements a and b in F a third element, called $a \times b$ or ab or $a \cdot b$, which is also in F);

(b) $(ab)c = a(bc)$ (*associative multiplication*; that is, parentheses may be introduced anywhere in a product);

(c) $ab = ba$ (*commutative multiplication*; that is, the order of the elements multiplied is immaterial);

(d) there exists an element 1 such that $a \cdot 1 = a$ (1 is called the unity element or the *multiplicative identity*);

(e) there exists, for every element $a \neq 0$ in F, an element called a^{-1} in F such that $aa^{-1} = 1$ (a^{-1} is called the *multiplicative inverse* of a);

(1.2.3) $a(b + c) = ab + ac$ (*distributive law* for multiplication over addition).

The laws for a field thus fall into three classes: five laws describing the behaviour of elements as regards addition, five analogous laws describing the behaviour of elements as regards multiplication, and one final law connecting addition and multiplication.

In elementary work, we assume that the integers, together with their algebraic properties as regards addition and multiplication, are known. Clearly the integers do not form a field, since, with the exception of $+1$ and -1, no integers have integral inverses. However, while the system of integers violates (1.2.2(e)), all the other requirements for a field are satisfied; indeed, this fact explains the origin of the field axioms (1.2.1), (1.2.2), and (1.2.3); they are an abstract formulation of the ordinary laws for working with numbers.

We shall now consider some common examples of fields (assuming that the system of integers and its properties is known).

Example 1.2.1. A rational number is the quotient a/b of two integers, where $b \neq 0$. Equality of rational numbers and the effect of the two binary operations are defined by the laws:

$$\frac{a}{b} = \frac{c}{d} \qquad \text{if and only if } ad = bc,$$

(1.2.4)
$$\frac{a}{b} + \frac{c}{d} = \frac{ad + bc}{bd},$$

$$\left(\frac{a}{b}\right)\left(\frac{c}{d}\right) = \frac{ac}{bd}.$$

All of the field laws can be easily checked; for example, to check (1.2.1(c)), we compute

$$\frac{a}{b} + \frac{c}{d} = \frac{ad + bc}{bd},$$

$$\frac{c}{d} + \frac{a}{b} = \frac{cb + ad}{db};$$

these two expressions are equal, since the commutative law does hold for addition and multiplication of integers.

Similarly, to check (1.2.2(e)), we note that the multiplicative inverse of a/b is the rational number b/a (for every rational number other than $0/b$).

Example 1.2.2. The real numbers (all infinite decimals) form a field with respect to the ordinary arithmetic operations of addition and multiplication.

Example 1.2.3. The complex numbers $a + bi$, where a and b are any real numbers and i is an abstract symbol satisfying the postulate $i^2 + 1 = 0$, form a field. Addition and multiplication of these complex numbers is to be performed formally, with i regarded as an algebraic symbol subject to the associative, commutative, and distributive laws.

As an illustration, we check some of the postulates for the complex field (assuming that we have already verified Example 1.2.2, that is, that the real number system is a field).

(1.2.2)(a)

$$\begin{aligned}(a + bi)(c + di) &= ac + adi + bci + bdi^2 \\ &= (ac - bd) + (ad + bc)i.\end{aligned}$$

This expression has the proper form and so the complex number system is closed under multiplication.

(1.2.2)(e) It is easy to check that the complex number $a + bi$ satisfies the equation ($ab \neq 0$)

$$(a + bi)\left[\frac{a}{a^2 + b^2} + \frac{(-b)}{a^2 + b^2}\, i\right] = 1 + 0i;$$

this result gives the multiplicative inverse of $a + bi$.

(1.2.2)(d) $0 + 0i$ is the additive identity.

Example 1.2.4. Let a system be defined to comprise two distinct elements, the words "odd" and "even". Define:

$$\begin{aligned}\text{odd} + \text{odd} &= \text{even}, & \text{odd} \times \text{odd} &= \text{odd},\\ \text{even} + \text{odd} &= \text{odd}, & \text{even} \times \text{odd} &= \text{even},\\ \text{even} + \text{even} &= \text{even}, & \text{even} \times \text{even} &= \text{even}.\end{aligned}$$

It is easy to verify that this system (notice that it does not contain numbers as its elements) is indeed a field; the additive identity is the word *even* which does not change any word when it is added to it; the multiplicative identity is the word *odd* which does not change any word when it multiplies it. This field is a very small and simple one, and should cause us no difficulty once we overcome our initial queasiness over defining addition and multiplication of words.

Example 1.2.5. Let a system be defined to comprise eleven distinct elements, namely, the integers $0, 1, 2, \ldots, 10$. Addition and multiplication are to be defined *modulo eleven*, that is, we work as in ordinary arithmetic but, as soon as a sum or product equals or exceeds 11, we throw away multiplies of 11 until we are left with a "number" in the system. For example,

$$8 + 7 = 4,$$

$$8 \times 7 = 1.$$

Thus, to "multiply 9 by 6", we think of the product 54, throw away 44, and are left with the answer 10.

It is easy to check that this system satisfies the postulates for a field; for example,

$$3^{-1} = 4, \qquad \text{since } 3 \times 4 = 1;$$

also,

$$5^{-1} = 9, \qquad \text{since } 5 \times 9 = 1.$$

EXERCISES

1. Verify Examples 1.2.1 and 1.2.3 in full.
2. Find the additive and multiplicative inverses of all elements in the field of Example 1.2.5.
3. Show that the numbers 0, 1, 2, 3, 4, form a field with addition and multiplication defined modulo 5; show that the numbers 0, 1, 2, 3, 4, 5, do not form a field with addition and multiplication defined modulo 6.
4. Show that all numbers of the form $a + b\sqrt{11}$, with a and b rational numbers, form a field.

1.3. SAMPLE THEOREMS ON FIELDS

Various trivial properties of fields can be proved at once from the field postulates; the following illustrations may be offered. These theorems are the sort that need never be stressed; one proves them once in a lifetime to show that they can be proved, and then desists quickly!

THEOREM 1.3.1. If $a \in F$, then $a \cdot 0 = 0$.

Proof.

$$a(b + 0) = ab + a \cdot 0,$$

$$a(b) = ab + a \cdot 0,$$

$$(-ab) + ab = (-ab) + (ab + a \cdot 0),$$

$$0 = [(-ab) + ab] + a \cdot 0,$$

$$0 = 0 + a \cdot 0 = a \cdot 0.$$

THEOREM 1.3.2. $(-1)a = -a.$

Proof.

$$\begin{aligned} a + (-a) &= 0, \\ &= 0 \cdot a, \\ &= [1 + (-1)]a, \\ &= 1 \cdot a + (-1)a, \\ &= a + (-1)a. \end{aligned}$$

Consequently,

$$\begin{aligned} (-a) + [a + (-a)] &= (-a) + [a + (-1)a], \\ [(-a) + a] + (-a) &= [(-a) + a] + (-1)a. \end{aligned}$$

Hence

$$\begin{aligned} 0 + (-a) &= 0 + (-1)a, \\ -a &= (-1)a. \end{aligned}$$

THEOREM 1.3.3. $ab = 0 \Rightarrow a = 0 \quad \text{or} \quad b = 0.$

Proof. $a = 0$ or $a \neq 0$.

If $a = 0$, the theorem is true.
If $a \neq 0$, a possesses an inverse a^{-1}.

Hence

$$\begin{aligned} a^{-1}(ab) &= a^{-1} \cdot 0 = 0, \\ (a^{-1}a)b &= 0, \\ 1 \cdot b &= 0, \\ b &= 0. \end{aligned}$$

Thus, we have shown that if $a \neq 0$, then $b = 0$; that is, either a or b must be zero.

At this stage, we might profitably say a few words about the place of the axiomatic approach in mathematics. In general, the creative and developmental stage of a branch of mathematics comes first; when this is largely complete, the axiomatic method is introduced as a *means of organization.* The axiomatic method tends to be dull and sterile if considered *per se*; it is merely a neat way of organizing a subject for presentation, once the subject has been largely worked out. Nothing can more quickly deaden interest in mathematics than a premature introduction of the axiomatic method; as one well-known mathematician has said, axiomatic checking of things such as the associative law of addition for rationals is "the sort of thing any mathematician could do, but which he would certainly strive to avoid doing". Furthermore, axiomatics can be one of the most dangerous kinds of mathematics for the secondary-school teacher. It appears easy, and consequently leads to ill-judged excesses. The following solution of a problem is quoted from a set of Grade 9 notes which have been used in one Ontario secondary school!

	["Authorities"]
$6x + 3x + 2y + 4x$	
$= 6x + 3x + 4x + 2y$	M_1, Thm. 2
$= x \cdot 6 + x \cdot 3 + x \cdot 4 + 2y$	M_2, S
$= x(6 + 3) + x \cdot 4 + 2y$	D, S
$= x \cdot 9 + x \cdot 4 + 2y$	A_1, S
$= x(9 + 4) + 2y$	D, S
$= x \cdot 13 + 2y$	A_1, S
$= 13x + 2y$	M_2, S
$\therefore\ 6x + 3x + 2y + 4x = 13x + 2y$	E_3

This elaborate list of "authorities" and the verbosity of the approach are typical of the sort of material which the "axiomatic disease" can produce. A true mathematician could almost be defined as one who felt repelled by the above "solution". I say "solution", since the "solution", while purporting to be very complete, lacks a number of applications of the associative law; furthermore, the ignoring of the right distributive law in favour of a cumbersome use of the left distributive law could certainly leave a student befuddled.

EXERCISES

1. Show that a single element z, subject to the laws $z + z = z \cdot z = z$, forms a field. We often call such a field consisting of a single element "the trivial field".
2. A *subfield* is defined to be a subset of a given field which is itself a field; for example, the real field is a subfield of the complex field. Does the set of all numbers $a + bi$, with a and b *rational*, form a subfield of the complex field?
3. Consider the field described in Example 1.2.5; is it a subfield of the rational field?
4. Prove that there is an infinite number of subfields of the real field by proving that all numbers $a + b\sqrt{m}$ (a and b rational, m an arbitrary integer not equal to a perfect square) form a field (cf. Exercise 4 of Section 1.2).
5. Show that the field of Example 1.2.5 has no subfields except the trivial subfield.
6. Let ϕ be the complex number
$$\phi = \tfrac{1}{2}(1 + \sqrt{3}\, i).$$
(Note that $\phi^2 - \phi + 1 = 0$.) Prove that all numbers of the form $a + b\phi$, where a and b are rational, form a subfield of the complex field.
7. Prove that every subfield of the real field (other than the trivial subfield) must contain all rational numbers (in this sense, the rational field is the smallest subfield of the real field, and therefore also of the complex field).

1.4. GROUPS

A less familiar structure than a field is a group. It is defined in the following manner.

A *group* G is a set of elements $a, b, c, \ldots$ with one binary operation θ such that

(1.4.1) $$a \,\theta\, b \in G$$

(the group is *closed* with respect to the operation θ),

(1.4.2) $$(a \,\theta\, b) \,\theta\, c = a \,\theta\, (b \,\theta\, c)$$

(*the associative law* holds with respect to θ),

(1.4.3) $$a \,\theta\, e = e \,\theta\, a = a$$

(for any $a \in G$, there is an identity element e),

(1.4.4) $$a \,\theta\, a^{-1} = a^{-1} \,\theta\, a = e$$

(for any $a \in G$, there is an inverse element a^{-1}).

If there is a further postulate

(1.4.5) $$a \,\theta\, b = b \,\theta\, a,$$

then we say the group is a *commutative* or *abelian* group.

The idea of a group can best be grasped from a few elementary examples. In all these cases, the postulates are easily checked.

Example 1.4.1. The set of all integers $\ldots, -3, -2, -1, 0, 1, 2, 3, \ldots,$ with the operation $+$ of addition, is an additive abelian group.

For it is clear that $a + b$ is in G (the sum of two integers is an integer), the associative law is one of the basic properties of integers, the integer 0 is the identity element (since $a + 0 = 0 + a = a$), the integer $(-a)$ is the inverse of a with respect to the operation $+$ [since $a + (-a) = (-a) + a = 0$].

Finally, we note that

$$a + b = b + a$$

for any two integers a and b; thus the integers are a commutative group with respect to the operation $+$.

Example 1.4.2. The set of all rational numbers a/b ($b \neq 0$) different from zero, with the operation $\times$ of multiplication is a group.

Example 1.4.3. The four complex numbers, $1, -1, \sqrt{-1}, -\sqrt{-1}$, with the operation of multiplication, is a *finite group*, since it contains only a finite number of elements.

Example 1.4.4. Consider a square *ABCD* rotating about its midpoint. The rotation R_α denotes a rotation through α degrees in a counter-clockwise direction. We consider the four rotations R_0, R_{90}, R_{180}, R_{270}; these rotations leave the square fixed in position, and we define the resultant of two rotations as the single rotation which produces the same result. Thus,

$$R_{180} \ \theta \ R_{270} = R_{90}$$

(a rotation of 180° followed by a rotation of 270° is equivalent to a rotation of 90°).

It is easy to verify that R_0 is the identity element, and that the inverse elements are given by the results

$$R_0 \ \theta \ R_0 \ \ = R_0,$$

$$R_{90} \ \theta \ R_{270} = R_0,$$

$$R_{180} \ \theta \ R_{180} = R_0.$$

Example 1.4.5. All of the preceding examples of groups have been commutative groups. We now illustrate a non-commutative group. Consider the square *ABCD* of the last example, and consider the following additional operations (see Figure 1.1):

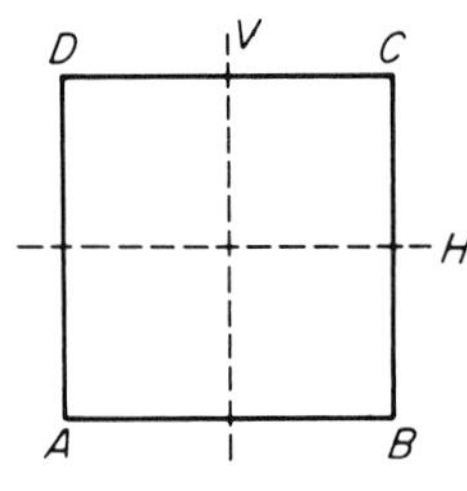

Figure 1.1

V (a reflection about the vertical line bisecting the square),

H (a reflection about the horizontal line bisecting the square),

D_1 (a reflection about the upward diagonal *AC*),

D_2 (a reflection about the downward diagonal *BD*).

It is easy to check that:

$R_{90} \ \theta \ V$ first carries the square into the position shown in Figure 1.2, and then into the position shown in Figure 1.3. But this final result could have been achieved by the single reflection D_1; thus, $R_{90} \ \theta \ V = D_1$.

Figure 1.2

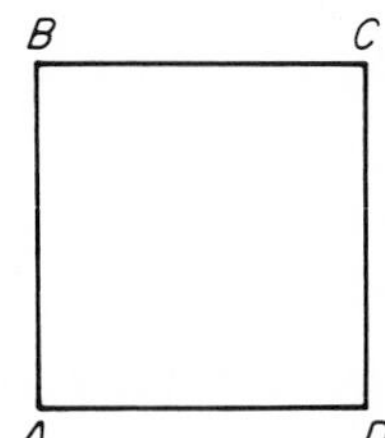

Figure 1.3

However, $V \theta R_{90}$ carries the square first into the position shown in Figure 1.4, and then into the position shown in Figure 1.5. We thus find $V \theta R_{90} = D_2$. These two computations show that the results $R_{90} \theta V$ and $V \theta R_{90}$ are different, that is, the group is not commutative.

Figure 1.4

Figure 1.5

The group concept allows us to give a much shorter definition for a field. We can say that a field F is a set of elements such that

(a) all elements form a commutative group with respect to the operation $+$,

(b) all elements, except 0, form a commutative group with respect to the operation $\times$,

(c) multiplication is distributive over addition according to the law:

$$a(b + c) = ab + ac.$$

EXERCISES

1. Prove that the set of all integral multiples

$$\ldots, -3m, -2m, -m, 0, m, 2m, 3m, \ldots$$

of a fixed integer m is a commutative group with respect to the operation $+$.

2. Let $\phi = \frac{1}{2}(1 + \sqrt{3}\, i)$; prove that $\phi, \phi^2, \phi^3, \phi^4, \phi^5, \phi^6$, form a commutative group with respect to the operation $\times$.

3. In Example 1.4.5, express as a single operation:

(a) $R_{90} \theta D_1$, (b) $R_{180} \theta V$,

(c) $R_{270} \theta H$, (d) $H \theta V$,

(e) $D_1 \theta V$, (f) $H \theta R_{270}$,

(g) $R_{90} \theta H \theta R_{90}$, (h) $H \theta V \theta D_1$.

4. It is quite common to call the operation θ of a group simply by the name "multiplication" (using "multiplication" in the extended sense of "combination").

Thus, in Example 1.4.5, we could write

$$V\,\theta\, R_{90} = V \cdot R_{90} = VR_{90} = D_2.$$

Using this convention, compute

(a) $R_{90}R_{90}R_{90}$, (b) $R_{270}D_1$,

(c) $V^5(= VVVVV)$, (d) $R_{270}{}^{-4}[= (R_{270}{}^{-1})^4]$,

(e) $(D_1H)^2$, (f) $(VR_{90})^3$.

[Note that $(D_1H)^2 = D_1H \cdot D_1H \neq D_1^2H^2$].

5. Consider an equilateral triangle ABC with altitudes AD, BE, CF concurrent at H (take AD as vertical).
Define the following operations (which leave ABC fixed in position).

R_0: a rotation about H through 0°,
R_{120}: a rotation about H through 120°,
R_{240}: a rotation about H through 240°,
A_1: a reflection in the altitude through the upper vertex,
A_2: a reflection in the altitude through the next counterclockwise vertex,
A_3: a reflection in the third altitude.

The "product" of two operations is defined as the single operation producing the equivalent result. Thus

$$R_{120}R_{240} = R_0; \qquad R_{120}A_1 = A_2.$$

Fill in the other products in the following *group multiplication table*, where the element which appears in the cell at the intersection of row x and column y is the product xy of the elements x and y which are used to label the row and the column respectively.

	R_0	R_{120}	R_{240}	A_1	A_2	A_3
R_0						
R_{120}			R_0	A_2		
R_{240}						
A_1						
A_2						
A_3						

6. Form the group multiplication table for the eight elements ± 1, $\pm p$, $\pm q$, $\pm pq$, given that p and q are abstract symbols obeying the associative law and the rules

$$p^2 = q^2 = -1, \qquad qp = -pq.$$

[Note that p and q are *not* numbers.] Furthermore, $+1$ and -1 follow the ordinary laws of algebra with respect to the other symbols.

For instance,

$$\begin{aligned} q(pq) &= (qp)q = (-pq)q \\ &= -p(q^2) = (-p)(-1) = p. \end{aligned}$$

1.5. ISOMORPHISMS

We shall conclude this chapter by introducing a very important concept concerning algebraic systems, the concept of isomorphism. The abstract definition of an isomorphism is:

An *isomorphism* is a mapping of one algebraic system S on a second system T such that:

(a) every element s in S has a unique image t in T;

(b) every element t in T is the image of a unique element s in S;

(c) specified relations holding between elements of S hold between their images in T. For example, if $s_1 \longrightarrow t_1, s_2 \longrightarrow t_2$, then $s_1 \,\theta\, s_2 \longrightarrow t_1 \,\theta\, t_2$ (we use the single arrow $\longrightarrow$ to denote a correspondence; thus the preceding relation is read: "If s_1 is mapped on t_1 and s_2 is mapped on t_2, then $s_1 \,\theta\, s_2$ is mapped on $t_1 \,\theta\, t_2$"; in other words, the image of a resultant is mapped on the resultant of the images).

In the preceding definition we have assumed that S and T have the same operation θ; if this is not the case, we make the operations in S and T correspond (there may even be more than one type of operation in S and T; cf. Exercise 1 below).

Example 1.5.1. As an illustration, consider the groups in Examples 1.4.3 and 1.4.4 of the preceding section. We can set up a one-to-one correspondence (denoted by a double-headed arrow) in the following manner.

(1.5.1) $\quad 1 \longleftrightarrow R_0, \quad -1 \longleftrightarrow R_{180}, \quad \sqrt{-1} \longleftrightarrow R_{90}, \quad -\sqrt{-1} \longleftrightarrow R_{270}.$

Then any relation holding in the one group has an exact counterpart in a relation in the other group; we note that

$$(-1) \times (-\sqrt{-1}) = \sqrt{-1},$$

and consequently, considering the images of these elements under the one-to-one correspondence (1.5.1),

$$R_{180} \,\theta\, R_{270} = R_{90}$$

(note that the operations $\times$ and θ in the two groups correspond).

From the mathematical point of view, these two groups behave in the same way (even though the elements in the groups, namely, complex numbers, as opposed to rotations, are very different). Thus we say that the two groups have the *same form* or are *isomorphic*.

If we make the group multiplication tables for these two groups, they appear as follows:

	1	-1	$\sqrt{-1}$	$-\sqrt{-1}$
1	1	-1	$\sqrt{-1}$	$-\sqrt{-1}$
-1	-1	1	$-\sqrt{-1}$	$\sqrt{-1}$
$\sqrt{-1}$	$\sqrt{-1}$	$-\sqrt{-1}$	-1	1
$-\sqrt{-1}$	$-\sqrt{-1}$	$\sqrt{-1}$	1	-1

	R_0	R_{180}	R_{90}	R_{270}
R_0	R_0	R_{180}	R_{90}	R_{270}
R_{180}	R_{180}	R_0	R_{270}	R_{90}
R_{90}	R_{90}	R_{270}	R_{180}	R_0
R_{270}	R_{270}	R_{90}	R_0	R_{180}

The isomorphism of these two tables is evidenced by the fact that, except for nomenclature, they are the same; for example, wherever -1 appears in the first table, its correspondent R_{180} appears in the second table, and vice versa.

Example 1.5.2. Consider the group S consisting of all positive real numbers under the operation multiplication; consider also the group T consisting of all real numbers under the operation addition. We set up a correspondence between S and T by the mapping

$$a \in S \longrightarrow \log_{10} a \in T;$$

conversely,

$$b \in T \longrightarrow 10^b \in S.$$

This correspondence is one-to-one; for instance,

$$2 \in S \longleftrightarrow .30103 \in T,$$

$$.002 \in S \longleftrightarrow -2.69897 \in T,$$

$$1 \in S \longleftrightarrow 0 \in T.$$

This correspondence is an isomorphism since, if a and b are any two elements of S, we have

$$a \longleftrightarrow \log_{10} a,$$

$$b \longleftrightarrow \log_{10} b,$$

$$ab \longleftrightarrow \log_{10} ab,$$

and

$$\log_{10} ab = \log_{10} a + \log_{10} b.$$

(Note that $\times$ is the operation in S, $+$ is the operation in T.)

Clearly isomorphism is a powerful concept which offers possibilities for giving a unified treatment to superficially different mathematical systems.

EXERCISES

1. Consider the field F of Example 1.2.4 comprising the words "odd" and "even"; define a field G to comprise the numbers 0 and 1 with addition and multiplication defined modulo 2, that is,

$$1 + 1 = 0, \qquad 0 + 0 = 0, \qquad 0 + 1 = 1;$$
$$1 \cdot 1 = 1, \qquad 1 \cdot 0 = 0, \qquad 0 \cdot 0 = 0.$$

Show that the fields F and G are isomorphic.

2. Show that the operations R_0, R_{120}, R_{240}, form a *subgroup* of the group in Exercise 1.4.5; then show that this group is isomorphic to the multiplicative group formed by the complex numbers β, β^2, β^3, where

$$\beta = \tfrac{1}{2}(-1 + \sqrt{3}\, i).$$

3. Let C be a circle and let R_α $(0 \leq \alpha < 360°)$ denote a rotation through α degrees about the centre (this leaves the circle fixed in position). Two rotations are combined in the usual manner; thus

$$R_{227}\, \theta\, R_{145} = R_{12}.$$

Show that R_0, R_{60}, R_{120}, R_{180}, R_{240}, R_{300} form a (finite) *subgroup* G of the infinite group of all rotations R_α. Then show that G is isomorphic to the group consisting of ϕ^x $(0 < x \leq 6)$ in Exercise 1.4.2.

4. Let S and T be defined as in Example 1.5.2. Show that

$$a \in S \longrightarrow \log_2 a \in T$$

is an isomorphism between S and T, and fill in the blanks in the following table:

$$2 \in S \longleftrightarrow \cdots \in T$$
$$\tfrac{1}{256} \in S \longleftrightarrow \cdots \in T$$
$$1 \in S \longleftrightarrow \cdots \in T$$
$$\cdots \in S \longleftrightarrow 3 \in T$$
$$\cdots \in S \longleftrightarrow -\tfrac{1}{2} \in T$$
$$\cdots \in S \longleftrightarrow 2.5 \in T$$
$$2.72 \in S \longleftrightarrow \cdots \in T$$
$$\cdots \in S \longleftrightarrow -3.02 \in T$$

2

Set Theory

Kenneth D. Fryer

2.1. FUNDAMENTALS

In any mathematical discussion or theory, we must know exactly what numbers, objects, or elements we are talking about. The collection of such objects in a particular discussion is called the *parent universe*, *universe*, or the *universal set U for that discussion*. Parent universes can be such widely differing collections as: all the people in a given room; all positive integers; all positive and negative integers and 0; all rational numbers (numbers of the form a/b where a and b are integers and $b \neq 0$); all real numbers (that is, all infinite decimals); all complex numbers (numbers of the form $a + bi$ where a and b are real numbers and i is an abstract symbol satisfying the postulate $i^2 + 1 = 0$); all points *inside* the circle $x^2 + y^2 = 4$; all the men in a given village who are shaved by the village barber; etc.

If the parent universe in a mathematical theory is not defined, errors may arise in the ensuing development. Thus, to say that the equation $x^2 + 4 = 0$ has no solution (as is done in some high school texts) is incorrect unless it is specified that the parent universe (from which solutions may be drawn) for the discussion is, say, the field of real numbers. If the parent universe for solutions were the field of complex numbers, the equation would have the roots $2i$ and $-2i$.

The notion of *set* is one of our basic undefined quantities, although we partially disguise this fact by saying that: A *set* M is a collection of objects, from a parent universe U, with the property that we can answer "Yes" or "No" to the question "Does any specified object x from U belong to the set M?" Clearly U itself is a set by this criterion.

Some fundamental sets are: the set I of positive and negative integers and zero; the set Ra of rational numbers; the set Re of real numbers; the set C of complex numbers (C is a parent universe for all these sets since any real number a can be identified with the complex number $a + 0i$).

Notice the two *requisites for a set M.*

(2.1.1) *A set M must consist of elements from some specified universe U.*

(2.1.2) *Every element of U either belongs to M or does not belong to M.*

There are times when the word "set" is incorrectly applied to collections of objects, and carelessness in this respect can lead to error. The following examples may serve to illustrate whether what might be called a "set" is actually a set or not.

Example 2.1.1. Let U consist of all the people living in Chicago. Then the collection of children living in Chicago would be a set in this parent universe. To speak of the "set" of university students in Chicago would be incorrect, since, presumably, some university students might commute from points outside Chicago, and thus would not be members of the parent universe. Thus, requirement (2.1.1) would be violated. To speak of the "set" of university students *living* in Chicago would be correct.

Example 2.1.2. Let U be the set of positive integers. Then the collection $\{1, 2, 3, 4, 5\}$ of positive integers is a set in U, but the collection consisting of all multiples of 5 is not, since $(-2)5$ would not be a member of U. However, the collection of multiples of 5 would be a set if the parent universe were the set I of all positive and negative integers and zero.

Example 2.1.3. Let U be the set Re of real numbers. Then the "set" M of all roots of all polynomial equations with integral coefficients is not a set, since the roots of the equation $x^2 + 1 = 0$ are not real numbers, and hence are not elements from the universe. M would be a set if the parent universe were the set C of complex numbers, since a basic theorem in algebra states that: "A polynomial equation of degree n with complex coefficients has exactly n complex roots". (Note that polynomials with complex coefficients include polynomials with integral coefficients, and complex roots include real roots as well.)

Example 2.1.4. Let U consist of all points *inside* the circle $x^2 + y^2 = 4$. Then the collection of all points inside the circle $x^2 + y^2 - 2x = 0$ can legitimately be called a set in this parent universe, but the collection of all points *on* the circle $x^2 + y^2 - 2x = 0$ can not, since the point (2, 0) is a point on this latter circle, but is not a point of the parent universe.

The misuses of the word *set* in the above examples have all been due to violations of the requirement (2.1.1); elements were involved which were not members of the parent universe. Example 2.1.5 will illustrate violation of the second requirement (2.1.2.)

Example 2.1.5. A certain emperor passes an edict that "all men in the village of Zik must be clean-shaven." This can come to pass only if the men either shave themselves or are shaved by the village barber, Mr. Schmydt. The imperial ukase further contains the clause [Clause 3F(a)] that "Mr. Schmydt shall shave a 'set' M of men comprising all those men (and only those men) who do not shave themselves".

Consider the universe U of all men in Zik, and let M be the "set" of all men referred to in Clause 3F(a); is M actually a set? Here, we may ask ourselves whether Mr. Schmydt belongs to M; if our answer is "Yes", we have a contradiction (since Mr. Schmydt shaves all men in M, he will have to shave himself; but he is only to shave men who do not shave themselves); but if our answer is "No", we have another contradiction (since then Mr. Schmydt is not in the set of men who do not shave themselves; thus, he must be shaved by the barber, that is, he does shave himself!).

Since we can not answer "Yes" or "No" unequivocally to the question "Is Mr. Schmydt himself a member of M?", we see that requirement (2.1.2) for a set is violated.

We can not stress too strongly the importance of having a clearly defined universe in a given mathematical discussion and of making sure that a collection described as a "set" actually is a set. One must insist upon an analytic approach of this nature to sets—one begins with a parent universe, and then works with sets contained in that universe. The suggestion has been made that Euclidean Geometry, as an example of a deductive system in secondary schools, might be replaced by Set Theory or Boolean Algebra because it is claimed that the usual Euclidean approach is incomplete and leads to paradoxes (see Chapter 10). However, incautious work with sets can lead to paradoxes just as bad or even worse. Those who criticize Euclid for not explicitly stating the axioms of order, superposition, etc., and yet themselves adopt a synthetic or "building-up" approach to sets will be simply replacing one incomplete system by another.

In many paradoxes, such as the Barber Paradox (a village barber shaves all the men in a village who do not shave themselves; does the barber shave himself?), a proper application of the criteria (2.1.1) and (2.1.2) will show that the so-called "sets" which allow us to deduce contradictions are not really sets at all (see Example 2.1.5). This in turn leads us to see that the paradox arises from an incorrect use of the English language—possibly a nonsensical statement such as "Tokyo is larger than any city in the world" (Tokyo is obviously not larger than itself). The semantic error in the Barber Paradox, the omission of the word "other" (a village barber shaves all the *other* men . . .), leads to the apparent contradiction.

2.2. NOTATION

A finite set (consisting of a finite number of elements) may be designated by simply enumerating the elements in the set, if the number of elements is small. Thus $\{1, 2, 3, 4, 5\}$ denotes the set consisting of the integers 1, 2, 3, 4, and 5. The set consisting of the integers from 1 to 1000 could be designated $\{1, 2, 3, \ldots, 1000\}$ if it were clear that . . . represented the integers from 4 to 999 inclusive.

Designation of an infinite set other than by simply describing the set (such as "the set of all positive integers" or "the set of all points inside the circle $x^2 + y^2 = 4$") presents difficulties. The former could be written $\{1, 2, 3, \ldots\}$, but the latter could not be so enumerated.

The so-called "set-builder" terminology is now favoured by some mathematicians. This employs the "set builder",

$$\{* \mid \ldots\},$$

to be read "the set of all elements $*$ such that . . . ."

Example 2.2.1. $\{x \mid 1 \leq x \leq 1000, x \in I\}$ is the set of all elements x such that x lies between 1 and 1000 inclusive in value, and x is an integer ($x \in I$ is read "x *belongs to* I, the set of integers"), that is, the set $\{1, 2, 3, \ldots, 1000\}$ referred to previously.

Example 2.2.2. $\{(x, y) \mid x^2 + y^2 < 4;\ x, y \in Re\}$ is the set of all pairs of real numbers ($x, y \in Re$) the sum of whose squares is less than 4, equivalently, the set of all points inside the circle $x^2 + y^2 = 4$. What is the universe?

Example 2.2.3. $\{(x, y) \mid x = y;\ x, y \in Re\}$ is the set of all points in the Cartesian plane lying upon the line $y = x$.

EXERCISES

In each of the following, check whether the so-called "set" is actually a set or not.

1. Let U be the field of rational numbers.

   (a) Consider the "set" of solutions of the equation

$$x^3 - x^2 - 2x + 2 = 0.$$

(b) Consider the "set" of integral solutions of the equation

$$x^3 - x^2 - 2x + 2 = 0.$$

2. Let U consist of all positive integers. Consider the "set" of prime numbers.

3. Let U consist of all points inside the circle $x^2 + y^2 = 16$.

   (a) Consider the "set" $\{(x, y) \mid x^2 + 4y^2 < 16;\ x, y \in Re\}$.

   (b) Consider the "set" $\{(x, y) \mid x^2 + 4y^2 \leq 16;\ x, y \in Re\}$.

   (c) Describe the "sets" in (a) and (b) in words.

4. Let U consist of all students who are now in their last year of high school.

   (a) Consider the "set" of these students who will be in first year university next year.

   (b) Consider the "set" of students who will be in first year university next year.

5. Every baseball team in a certain city has a coach who may or may not be a playing member of his team. A new team is formed of all those coaches who are not playing members of the teams they coach. Is the coach of this team a playing member of the team? (Let U be the collection of all coaches; let M be the "set" of coaches who are not playing members of the teams they coach.)

2.3. THE NULL SET AND SUBSETS

One of the most important sets is the *null set* or *empty set*, usually called 0, but sometimes referred to as ϕ; it has the property that the question "Is x a member of 0?" must be answered "No" for all x in U. For example,

$$\{x \mid x^2 + 1 = 0;\ x \in Re\} = 0,$$

that is, the set of all real numbers x such that $x^2 + 1 = 0$ is the empty set (the universe here is the field Re of real numbers).

Two sets M and N are *equal* if and only if they have exactly the same elements; thus $\{1, 2, 3, 4\} = \{4, 2, 1, 3\}$ (we make no distinction as to the order of the elements; our definition involves only their occurrence).

If a set N has the property that every element of N is also a member of a set M, we say that N is a *subset* of M and write

$$N \subseteq M \qquad \text{(read: } N \text{ is contained in or equal to } M)$$

or

$$M \supseteq N \qquad \text{(read: } M \text{ contains or equals } N).$$

If N is a subset of M but does not equal M (M contains elements not in N), we write $N \subset M$ or $M \supset N$.

It is clear that U is a subset of itself under this definition; indeed, every set M contains itself as a subset, and we agree that every set shall contain the empty set 0 as a subset; these subsets we term *improper* subsets (the null set is also called a *trivial* subset of M).

Finally, a single element x of a set M is a subset of M, and we might write $x \subseteq M$ although in such a situation it is more usual to write $x \in M$ (x belongs to set M).

Example 2.3.1. If

$$M = \{\text{all multiples of } 5\},$$

then

$$N = \{\text{all multiples of } 10\}$$

is a proper subset of M, $N \subset M$. The set $\{0\}$ is also a proper subset of M, but note that $\{0\} \neq 0$ (0 is the empty subset, the subset consisting of *no* multiples of 5, whereas $\{0\}$ consists of the multiple $0 \cdot 5 = 0$).

Example 2.3.2. If M is the set of all points in the Euclidean plane, then

$$\{\text{all points on the line } y = x\},$$

$$\{\text{all points on or inside the ellipse } 9x^2 + 4y^2 = 36\},$$

$$\{\text{the origin } (0, 0)\},$$

are all proper subsets of M. The empty set is the set consisting of no points in the Euclidean plane.

EXERCISES

1. Give examples of subsets and define the empty set for each of the following universes:
   (a) the set of Presidents of the United States,
   (b) the set of points inside the circle $x^2 + y^2 = 25$,
   (c) the set of baseball players in the American League,
   (d) the set of real numbers.

2.4. OPERATIONS WITH SETS

Whenever we refer to two sets M and N, it will be understood that they are both from the same universe U. We now define the *complement* and *relative complement* of a set and the *intersection*, *union*, and *symmetric difference* of two sets.

DEFINITION. The *intersection* $M \cap N$ of two sets M and N is the set consisting of those elements common to both M and N. Thus, $M \cap N$ is a subset of both M and N, that is, $M \cap N \subseteq M$ and $M \cap N \subseteq N$. If $M \cap N = 0$ (M and N have no elements in common), we say that M and N are *disjoint* sets. We shall also use the alternative notation MN to represent the intersection $M \cap N$.

DEFINITION. The *union* $M \cup N$ of two sets M and N is the set consisting of all those elements occurring in at least one of M and N. Thus M and N are both subsets of $M \cup N$, that is, $M \subseteq M \cup N$ and $N \subseteq M \cup N$.

Definition. The *complement* $M' = \mu$ (the corresponding Greek lower-case letter is often used to denote the complement of any set given by a Roman capital letter) of a set M is the set of all elements of U not in M.

Definition. The *relative complement* $M - N$ of a set N with respect to M is the set of all elements of M not in N (for example, $M' = U - M$).

Definition. The *symmetric difference* $M \Delta N$ of two sets M and N is the set of all elements in either M or N but not in both. In terms of the previous operations,

$$M \Delta N = (M \cup N) - (M \cap N).$$

Note from the definition that $M \Delta N = N \Delta M$.

Example 2.4.1. If U is the set of positive integers, $M = \{1, 2, 3, 4, 5\}$, and $N = \{4, 5, 6, 7\}$, then

(a) $M \cap N = \{4, 5\}$,

(b) $M \cup N = \{1, 2, 3, 4, 5, 6, 7\}$,

(c) $M' = \{6, 7, 8, \ldots\}$,

(d) $M - N = \{1, 2, 3\}$,

(e) $M \Delta N = \{1, 2, 3, 6, 7\}$.

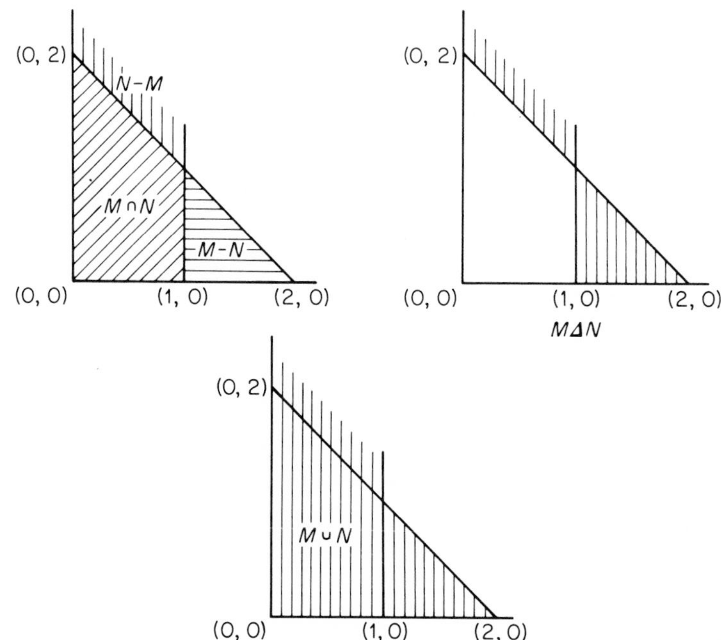

Figure 2.1

Example 2.4.2. Suppose that in one discussion the universe consists of the numbers $1, 2, 3, i, -i$, and that $M = \{1, 2, 3\}$; suppose that in a second discussion the universe is the field of real numbers and N is the set of roots of the equation $(x - 1)(x - 2)(x - 3) = 0$; then $M = N$, but $\mu \neq \nu$, since $\mu = M' = \{i, -i\}$ and $\nu = N' = \{$all real numbers except the integers $1, 2, 3\}$.

Example 2.4.3. Let the universe consist of all points in the first quadrant of the Euclidean plane. Let M consist of those points inside the first quadrant region bounded by the coordinate axes and the line $x + y = 2$ and N consist of those points inside the first quadrant region bounded by the coordinate axes and the line $x = 1$. Then $M \cap N$, $M \cup N$, $M - N$, $N - M$, and $M \Delta N$ comprise the points inside the shaded areas shown in Figure 2.1. What are M' and N'?

EXERCISES

1. Let U be the set of all positive integers, M the set of all even positive integers, and N the set of all odd positive integers. What are the sets $M \cap N$, $M \cup N$, M', N', $M - N$, $N - M$, and $M \Delta N$?
2. Let U be the set of all points in the Euclidean plane inside the rectangle bounded by the lines $x = \pm 5$, $y = \pm 5$; M the set of points inside the circle $x^2 + y^2 = 4$; N the set of points inside the circle $x^2 + y^2 - 4x = 0$. Use diagrams to represent the sets $M \cap N$, $M \cup N$, M', N', $M - N$, $N - M$, and $M \Delta N$.

2.5. GRAPHICAL REPRESENTATION OF SETS

We may represent the universe U by the points in and on a closed curve (usually a rectangle) and subsets $M, N, \ldots$ of U by points in and on closed curves (usually circles or ellipses) contained in the rectangle (see, for example, Figures 2.2 and 2.3). Such diagrams are called *Venn diagrams* after John Venn (1834–1883).

In working Exercise 2 of the preceding set of exercises, the reader essentially has been using Venn diagrams to represent the required subsets.

Note that, in Figure 2.2, sets A and B divide U into four regions, namely,

(1) AB or $A \cap B$ (double shading);

(2) $A\beta$ or $A \cap \beta$ or $A \cap B'$ (horizontal shading only);

(3) αB or $\alpha \cap B$ or $A' \cap B$ (vertical shading only);

(4) $\alpha\beta$ or $\alpha \cap \beta$ or $A' \cap B'$ (clear).

Clearly from the diagram, $A \Delta B = A\beta \cup \alpha B$.

In Figure 2.3, the sets A, B, and C divide U into eight regions, namely,

$$ABC,\ \alpha BC,\ A\beta C,\ AB\gamma,\ \alpha\beta C,\ \alpha B\gamma,\ A\beta\gamma,\ \alpha\beta\gamma.$$

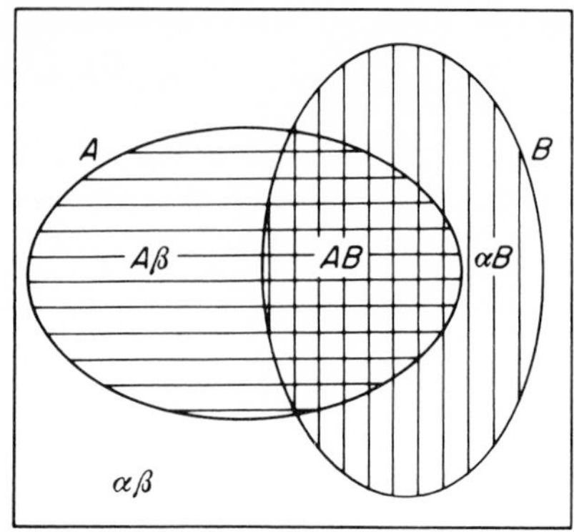

Figure 2.2

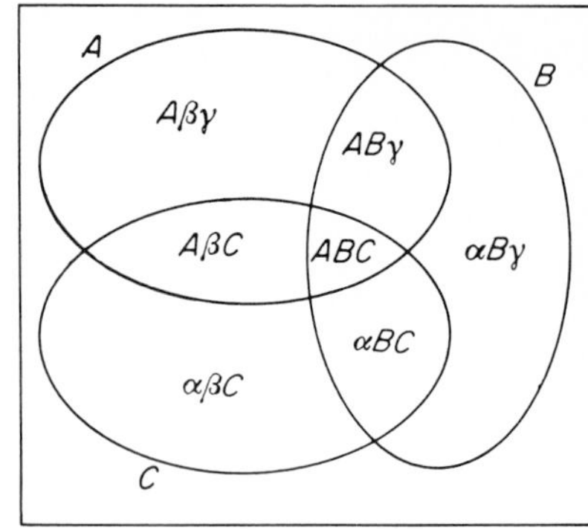

Figure 2.3

These two examples of sets and subsets will be discussed further in Section 2.7 under the heading "Ultimate Sets".

EXERCISES

1. Make a Venn diagram to illustrate that $A(B \cup C)$ and $AB \cup AC$ are the same sets.
2. Make Venn diagrams
   (a) with two sets A, B; $A\beta$ empty;
   (b) with three sets A, B, and C; αBC and $\alpha\beta C$ empty.

2.6. ALGEBRA OF SETS

Let A, B, and C be subsets of U; then the following relations or laws hold.

Complementation Laws

(2.6.1)
(a) $U' = 0$, (b) $0' = U$,
(c) $A \cap A' = 0$, *(d) $A \cup A' = U$,
*(e) $(A')' = A$.

Identity Laws

(2.6.2)
*(a) $A \cap U = A$, *(b) $A \cap 0 = 0$,
*(c) $A \cup U = U$, (d) $A \cup 0 = A$,
(e) $A - 0 = A$, (f) $A - A = 0$.

Idempotent Laws

(2.6.3) (a) $A \cap A = A$, (b) $A \cup A = A$.

Commutative Laws

(2.6.4) *(a) $A \cap B = B \cap A$, (b) $A \cup B = B \cup A$.

Associative Laws

(2.6.5) *(a) $(A \cap B) \cap C = A \cap (B \cap C)$,
(b) $(A \cup B) \cup C = A \cup (B \cup C)$.

Distributive Laws

(2.6.6) *(a) $A \cap (B \cup C) = (A \cap B) \cup (A \cap C)$,
(b) $A \cup (B \cap C) = (A \cup B) \cap (A \cup C)$.

Miscellaneous Relations

(2.6.7) *(a) $(A \cap B)' = A' \cup B'$, (b) $(A \cup B)' = A' \cap B'$,
*(c) $A - B = A \cap B'$, (d) $(A \cap B) \cup (A - B) = A$,
(e) $(A \cap B) \cap (A - B) = 0$.

These are the main relations in set theory involving the operations of intersection, union, complementation, and relative complementation. These

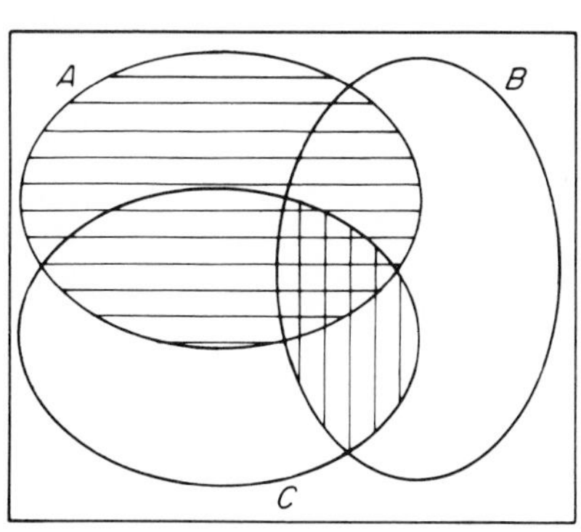

Fig. 2.4 $A \cup (B \cap C)$

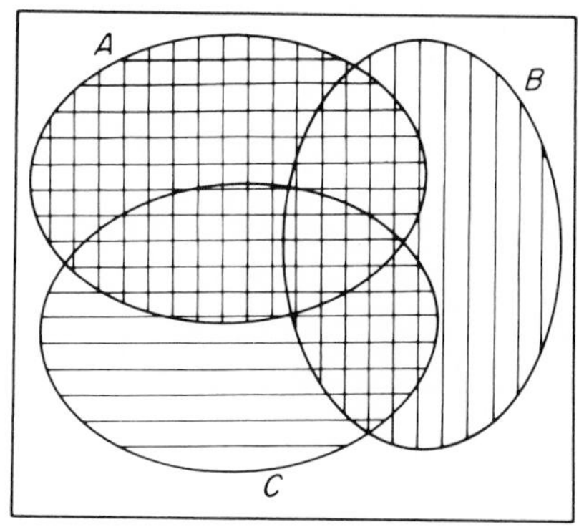

Fig. 2.5 $(A \cup B) \cap (A \cup C)$

relations may all be justified quite readily by means of Venn diagrams, and such diagrams are quite useful as aids to remembering these relations and possibly to developing other relations. However, it must be remembered that an actual proof for any relation must be more formal. We illustrate this in the following examples.

Example 2.6.1. Verify relation (2.6.6(b)),

$$A \cup (B \cap C) = (A \cup B) \cap (A \cup C).$$

From the Venn diagrams in Figures 2.4 and 2.5, we see that $A \cup (B \cap C)$, the total shaded area in Figure 2.4, is indeed equal to $(A \cup B) \cap (A \cup C)$, the crosshatched area in Figure 2.5. These diagrams justify relation

(2.6.6(b)), and would lead us to express

$$A \cup (B \cap C) \text{ as } (A \cup B) \cap (A \cup C)$$

or even as, say, $A \cup [(B \cap C) - A]$.

A formal proof of the relation (2.6.6(b)) is actually given as follows. We show that every element of the set $A \cup (B \cap C)$ is a member of the set $(A \cup B) \cap (A \cup C)$, that is,

$$A \cup (B \cap C) \subseteq (A \cup B) \cap (A \cup C),$$

and that every element of the set $(A \cup B) \cap (A \cup C)$ is a member of the set $A \cup (B \cap C)$, that is,

$$(A \cup B) \cap (A \cup C) \subseteq A \cup (B \cap C);$$

combining these two results will give $A \cup (B \cap C) = (A \cup B) \cap (A \cup C)$.

Assume $x \in A \cup (B \cap C)$; this fact implies, in turn, each of the following statements.

(1) $x \in A$ *or* $x \in B \cap C$;

(2) $x \in A$ *or* $[x \in B$ and $x \in C]$;

(3) $x \in A$ or B *and* $x \in A$ or C;

(4) $x \in A \cup B$ *and* $x \in A \cup C$;

(5) $x \in (A \cup B) \cap (A \cup C)$;

thus $A \cup (B \cap C) \subseteq (A \cup B) \cap (A \cup C)$.

Now assume conversely that $y \in (A \cup B) \cap (A \cup C)$; this fact implies, in turn, each of the following statements.

(1) $y \in A \cup B$ *and* $y \in A \cup C$;

(2) $y \in A$ or B *and* $y \in A$ or C;

(3) $y \in A$ *or* $y \in B$ and C;

(4) $y \in A$ *or* $y \in B \cap C$;

(5) $y \in A \cup (B \cap C)$.

Thus

$$(A \cup B) \cap (A \cup C) \subseteq A \cup (B \cap C);$$

so

$$A \cup (B \cap C) = (A \cup B) \cap (A \cup C).$$

Example 2.6.2. Verify relation (2.6.7(d)),

$$(A \cap B) \cup (A - B) = A.$$

The Venn diagram in Figure 2.6 immediately justifies this relation. Proceeding formally, we first prove relation (2.6.7(c)),

$$A - B = A \cap B'.$$

Let $x \in A - B$; then $x \in A$, but $x \bar{\in} B$ (x does not belong to B); thus $x \in A$ and $x \in B'$, that is, $x \in A \cap B'$; so

$$A - B \subseteq A \cap B'.$$

Now let $y \in A \cap B'$; then $y \in A$ and $y \in B'$. Hence $y \in A$ and $y \bar{\in} B$, that is, $y \in A - B$; so

$$A \cap B' \subseteq A - B.$$

It follows that $A - B = A \cap B'$.

Hence, we may prove (2.6.7(d)) by proving that

$$(A \cap B) \cup (A \cap B') = A.$$

Let $x \in (A \cap B) \cup (A \cap B')$; this fact implies, in turn, the following statements.

(1) $x \in A \cap B$ *or* $x \in A \cap B'$;

(2) $x \in A$ and B *or* $x \in A$ and B';

in any event, $x \in A$; so

$$(A \cap B) \cup (A \cap B') \subseteq A.$$

Now let $y \in A$; then either $y \in B$ or $y \in B'$, that is , $y \in A$ and B *or* $y \in A$ and B'; thus

$$y \in (A \cap B) \cup (A \cap B'),$$

that is,

$$A \subseteq (A \cap B) \cup (A \cap B').$$

It follows that

$$(A \cap B) \cup (A \cap B') = A.$$

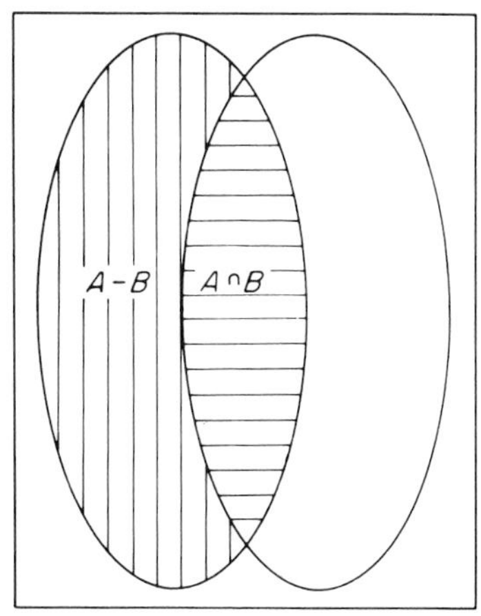

Fig. 2.6 $(A \cap B) \cup (A - B) = A$

As an exercise, the reader should prove the remaining relations in (2.6.1)–(2.6.7).

The relations (2.6.1)–(2.6.7) are not all independent; some may be proved algebraically from others. For example, if we prove the relations marked with an asterisk, using the method of proof illustrated in the examples, the remaining relations can be obtained algebraically from them. We illustrate this procedure in the following examples.

Example 2.6.3. Deduce

$$(A \cup B)' = A' \cap B'$$

from the starred relations.

From (2.6.7(a)), with A' and B' in place of A and B, and using (2.6.1(e)), we have

$$(A' \cap B')' = A \cup B;$$

hence

$$[(A' \cap B')']' = A' \cap B' = (A \cup B)',$$

from another application of (2.6.1(e)).

Example 2.6.4. Deduce (2.6.6(b)) from the starred relations of (2.6.1)–(2.6.7) and relation (2.6.7(b)) established in Example 2.6.3.

$$\begin{aligned} [A \cup (B \cap C)]' &= A' \cap (B \cap C)' && (2.6.7(b)) \\ &= A' \cap (B' \cup C') && (2.6.7(a)) \\ &= (A' \cap B') \cup (A' \cap C') && (2.6.6(a)) \\ &= (A \cup B)' \cup (A \cup C)' && (2.6.7(b)). \end{aligned}$$

Then

$$\{[A \cup (B \cap C)]'\}' = A \cup (B \cap C) \qquad (2.6.1(e)),$$

and also

$$\begin{aligned} \{[A \cup (B \cap C)]'\}' &= [(A \cup B)' \cup (A \cup C)']' \\ &= (A \cup B) \cap (A \cup C) && (2.6.7(b)). \end{aligned}$$

The required result then follows, namely,

$$A \cup (B \cap C) = (A \cup B) \cap (A \cup C).$$

Example 2.6.5. Deduce (2.6.1(b)) from the starred relations of (2.6.1)–(2.6.7).

$$U' \cap 0 = 0 \qquad (2.6.2(b)), \text{ with } A = U'.$$

So

$$[U' \cap 0]' = U \cup 0' = 0' \qquad (2.6.7(a)) \text{ and } (2.6.1(e)),$$

and also

$$U \cup 0' = U \qquad (2.6.2(c)) \text{ with } A = 0'.$$

It follows that $0' = U$, as required.

Example 2.6.6. Deduce (2.6.7(e)) from the starred relations of (2.6.1)–(2.6.7).

$$\begin{aligned} (A \cap B) \cup (A - B) &= (A \cap B) \cup (A \cap B') && (2.6.7(c)) \\ &= A \cap (B \cup B') && (2.6.6(a)) \\ &= A \cap U && (2.6.1(d)) \\ &= A && (2.6.1(a)). \end{aligned}$$

The reader should, as an exercise, prove algebraically the remaining ten unstarred relations, using the starred relations and previously proved unstarred relations.

2.7. POSITIVE AND ULTIMATE SETS

Given n sets $A, B, C, \ldots, N$, in a universe U, the *positive sets* are the $2^n - 1$ possible intersections of the n sets, together with the universe U, making a total of 2^n positive sets (you will be asked to verify this total in the Exercises). For example, if $n = 2$, the 2^2 positive sets are A, B, AB, and U; for $n = 3$, the 2^3 positive sets are A, B, C, AB, BC, CA, ABC, and U.

Again, from the n sets $A, B, C, \ldots, N$, in U there are 2^n sets, called *ultimate sets*, which can be formed by intersecting n sets from $A, B, C, \ldots, N$, $\alpha, \beta, \gamma, \ldots, \nu$, under the proviso that no set may occur with its complement. Thus, if $n = 2$, the ultimate sets are AB, αB, $A\beta$, and $\alpha\beta$; if $n = 3$, the ultimate sets are ABC, αBC, $A\beta C$, $AB\gamma$, $\alpha\beta C$, $\alpha B\gamma$, $\alpha\beta\gamma$, $A\beta\gamma$.

The ultimate sets are mutually disjoint, since if two ultimate sets contain different letters, then one must contain in its expression the complement of a set in the expression for the other; the intersection of the two sets will thus include the intersection of a set with its complement; this intersection is 0. For example,

$$\alpha B\gamma \cdot \alpha\beta\gamma = \alpha B\beta\gamma = 0,$$

since $B\beta = 0$. The positive sets are, of course, not necessarily mutually disjoint.

We define the *frequency* (A) associated with a set A to be the number of elements in the set A. As we shall see in the next section, it is sometimes the number of elements in a set that is of importance, and, if it is clear from the context, A may be used to indicate the frequency associated with A rather than the more awkward notation (A).

We state without proof the basic

THEOREM 2.7.1. The frequencies for the 2^n positive sets from the n sets $A, B, C, \ldots, N$, can be expressed algebraically in terms of the frequencies for the 2^n ultimate sets from $A, B, C, \ldots, N, \alpha, \beta, \gamma, \ldots, \nu$, and vice versa.

We illustrate the truth of this theorem for $n = 3$ in

Example 2.7.1. Express the frequencies of the eight positive sets formed from A, B, C, U, in terms of the frequencies of the ultimate sets formed from A, B, C, α, β, γ, and vice versa.

Such relations can be obtained with the aid of Venn diagrams (see Figure 2.3), or can be obtained algebraically, as follows.

(a) $(\alpha BC) =$ number of elements in BC which are not also in A

$$= (BC) - (ABC).$$

If we agree to use the set symbol to represent the frequency of the set, this result may be obtained algebraically as follows.

$$\alpha BC = (U - A)BC = UBC - ABC = BC - ABC.$$

Similarly,

(b) $A\beta C = A(U - B)C = AUC - ABC = AC - ABC$;

(c) $AB\gamma = AB(U - C) = ABU - ABC = AB - ABC$.

Again,

(d) $(\alpha\beta C) =$ number of elements in αC but not also in B

$= (\alpha C) - (\alpha BC)$

$=$ (number of elements in C but not in A) $- (\alpha BC)$

$= (C) - (AC) - (BC) + (ABC)$, using (a) above.

This result is obtained algebraically as follows:

$$\begin{aligned}\alpha\beta C &= (U - A)(U - B)C \\ &= UUC - AUC - UBC + ABC \\ &= C - AC - BC + ABC.\end{aligned}$$

Similarly,

(e) $$\begin{aligned}\alpha B\gamma &= (U - A)B(U - C) \\ &= UBU - UBC - ABU + ABC \\ &= B - BC - AB + ABC.\end{aligned}$$

(f) $$\begin{aligned}A\beta\gamma &= A(U - B)(U - C) \\ &= AUU - ABU - AUC + ABC \\ &= A - AB - AC + ABC.\end{aligned}$$

Finally,

(g) $(\alpha\beta\gamma) =$ number of elements in $\alpha\beta$ but not also in C

$= (\alpha\beta) - (\alpha\beta C)$

$=$ (number of elements in α but not in B) $- (\alpha\beta C)$

$= (\alpha) - (\alpha B) - (\alpha\beta C)$

$=$ (number of elements in U not in A)

$-$ (number of elements in B but not also in A)

$- (\alpha\beta C)$

$= (U) - (A) - [(B) - (AB)]$

$- [(C) - (AC) - (BC) + (ABC)]$,

using the expression for $(\alpha\beta C)$ given in (d).
Thus

$$\alpha\beta\gamma = (U) - (A) - (B) - (C) + (AB) + (BC) + (CA) - (ABC).$$

Algebraically,

$$\begin{aligned}\alpha\beta\gamma &= (U - A)(U - B)(U - C) \\ &= UUU - AUU - UBU - UUC + ABU + UBC + UCA - ABC \\ &= U - A - B - C + AB + BC + CA - ABC.\end{aligned}$$

We might point out here that

$$\begin{aligned}(A \cup B \cup C) &= (U - A'B'C') \\ &= (\alpha\beta\gamma)' = (U) - (\alpha\beta\gamma);\end{aligned}$$

so that the number of elements in $A \cup B \cup C$ is

$$A \cup B \cup C = A + B + C - AB - BC - CA + ABC.$$

If we continue to use the set symbols to represent set frequencies, we may obtain the following expressions for the positive sets in terms of ultimate sets:

(a) $AB = ABU = AB(C + \gamma) = ABC + AB\gamma,$

(b) $BC = UBC = (A + \alpha)BC = ABC + \alpha BC,$

(c) $AC = AUC = A(B + \beta)C = ABC + A\beta C,$

(d) $A = AUU = A(B + \beta)(C + \gamma)$
$\quad = ABC + AB\gamma + A\beta C + A\beta\gamma,$

(e) $B = UBU = (A + \alpha)B(C + \gamma)$
$\quad = ABC + AB\gamma + \alpha BC + \alpha B\gamma,$

(f) $C = UUC = (A + \alpha)(B + \beta)C$
$\quad = ABC + A\beta C + \alpha BC + \alpha\beta C,$

(g) $U = UUU = (A + \alpha)(B + \beta)(C + \gamma)$
$\quad = ABC + AB\gamma + A\beta C + A\beta\gamma + \alpha BC + \alpha B\gamma + \alpha\beta C + \alpha\beta\gamma.$

EXERCISES

1. Use set-theoretic considerations to verify the above algebraic manipulations giving the frequencies of the positive sets in terms of the frequencies of the ultimate sets.

2. Verify that 2^n positive sets can be formed from n sets $A, B, C, \ldots, N$, in a universe U.

3. Verify that 2^n ultimate sets can be formed from n sets $A, B, C, \ldots, N$, together with their complements.

In Exercises 4, 5, and 6, the set symbol will represent the frequency of the set.

4. Express (a) $\beta\gamma$, (b) AC, (c) $A\beta$, (d) αB, in terms of ultimate sets formed from A, B, C, and their complements.

5. Express (a) $A\beta C\delta$, (b) $\alpha\beta C\delta$, and (c) $\alpha BC\delta$, in terms of positive sets formed from A, B, C, D.

6. Express (a) AC, (b) ABD, (c) A, (d) U, in terms of ultimate sets formed from A, B, C, D, and their complements.

2.8. APPLICATIONS OF SET THEORY

An important application of the results of the preceding section occurs in the study of qualitative data in which objects are described not by measurements but by their possession or lack of a certain attribute. Thus, if A is the set of persons with blue eyes, B the set of males, and C the set of persons with fair hair, we see that these attributes divide the entire parent universe into eight classes—the ultimate sets; for example, ABC is the set of blue-eyed fair-haired males, $A\beta C$ is the set of blue-eyed fair-haired females, $AB\gamma$ the set of blue-eyed males without fair hair (note that γ is the set of persons without fair hair—persons with dark hair, red hair, or no hair at all!), etc.

Inconsistent data are sometimes presented to the public, as a result of commercial or economic surveys, and ultimate sets can often be used to detect inconsistencies. The data are described by the use of set theory, the universe is divided into ultimate sets, and the following criterion is used. *A necessary and sufficient condition for the consistency of the data is that the ultimate sets all contain non-negative numbers of elements.*

The use of this criterion will now be illustrated.

Example 2.8.1. In a recent survey of 500 men, 400 were reported as smokers and 200 as chewers of gum; 75 were listed as both smokers and gum chewers. Test the consistency of these data.

Let U be the set of men questioned (500). We divide the universe into positive sets (the numbers in parentheses refer to the number of men in each positive set), express the ultimate sets of U in terms of the positive sets, and thus determine the number of men in each ultimate set.

Let A be the set of smokers (400), B the set of gum chewers (200); then AB is the set of men who smoke and chew gum (75).

The ultimate sets (other than AB) are populated as follows:

$$A\beta = A(U - B) = A - AB = 325;$$

$$\alpha B = (U - A)B = B - AB = 125;$$

$$\alpha\beta = (U - A)(U - B) = U - A - B + AB = -25.$$

The fact that the set of non-smokers, non-chewers, contains a negative number of men indicates that the data are inconsistent.

Example 2.8.2. A recent poll of 500 men and 500 women indicated a total of 650 married persons; of these, 275 were men, and 500 of these married persons claimed to be happy. Of a total of 750 who claimed to be happy, 400 were men, and of these 200 were married. Check these data for consistency.

Let (a) U be the set of men and women polled (1000),

(b) A be the set of men (500),

(c) B be the set of married people (650),

(d) C be the set of happy people (750).

Then

(e) AB is the set of married men (275),

(f) BC is the set of happily married people (500),

(g) AC is the set of happy men (400),

(h) ABC is the set of happily married men (200).

The ultimate set frequencies can then be found.

(a) $\alpha BC = BC - ABC = 300,$

(b) $A\beta C = AC - ABC = 200,$

(c) $AB\gamma = AB - ABC = 75,$

(d) $\alpha\beta C = C - AC - BC + ABC = 50,$

(e) $\alpha B\gamma = B - AB - BC + ABC = 75,$

(f) $A\beta\gamma = A - AB - AC + ABC = 25,$

(g) $\alpha\beta\gamma = U - A - B - C + AB + AC + BC - ABC = 75.$

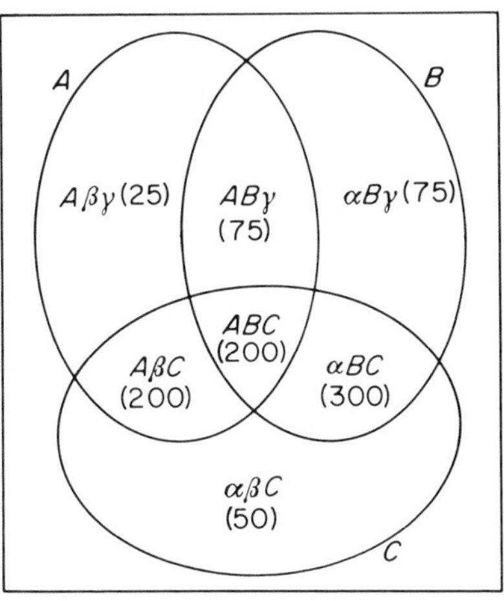

Figure 2.7

Thus the data are consistent. Note that the frequencies of the ultimate sets can be read from a Venn diagram in this particular example (see Figure 2.7). The frequencies of the positive sets A, B, C, AB, BC, CA, ABC, and U are entered, and those of the ultimate sets can then be easily calculated.

Example 2.8.3. The most recent census of Lower Slobbovia revealed the following information: "Of the total population of 1000, only 250 are happy with the government and 600 plan to emigrate immediately; of the 600 males, 150 are happy with the government and 150 plan to emigrate immediately; of the people who plan to emigrate, only 400 are unhappy with the government; finally, the men who are unhappy with the government and planning to emigrate are all the members of the all-male, 75-man government". Test these data for consistency.

Let U be the set of Lower Slobbovians (1000),

A be the set of people not happy with the government (750),

B be the set of males (600),

C be the set of those planning to emigrate (600).

Then

AB is the set of unhappy males (450),

AC is the set of unhappy people planning to emigrate (400),

BC is the set of males planning to emigrate (150),

ABC is the set of unhappy males planning to emigrate (75).

It follows that

$$\alpha BC = (U - A)BC = BC - ABC \quad (75),$$
$$AB\gamma = AB - ABC \quad (375),$$
$$A\beta C = AC - ABC \quad (325),$$
$$A\beta\gamma = A - AB - AC + ABC \quad (-25),$$
$$\alpha B\gamma = B - AB - BC + ABC \quad (75),$$
$$\alpha\beta C = C - AC - BC + ABC \quad (125),$$
$$\alpha\beta\gamma = U - A - B - C + AB + AC + BC - ABC \quad (-25).$$

We conclude that the data are inconsistent since $A\beta\gamma$ and $\alpha\beta\gamma$ contain negative numbers of elements. However, since everything in Lower Slobbovia is inconsistent, it might be argued that these data *are* consistent!

Example 2.8.4. Suppose that it is known that

(a) there are more single than married women in Chicago,
(b) there are more married women with fur coats than unmarried women without them,
(c) there are fewer single women with fur coats and their appendixes removed than married women without fur coats and without appendectomies.

Is the number of fur-coated spinsters with no operation greater than the number of un-coated and de-appendicized married women?

Let A be the set of married women in Chicago, B the set of women with fur coats, and C the set of women with appendixes removed.

The given conditions are

(a) $\alpha > A$,

(b) $AB > \alpha\beta$,

(c) $A\beta\gamma > \alpha BC$.

Then

$$\alpha = \alpha U = \alpha(B + \beta) = \alpha B + \alpha\beta,$$

$$A = AU = A(B + \beta) = AB + A\beta.$$

Hence, applying (a) and (b), we have $\alpha B > A\beta$. Also,

$$\alpha B = \alpha B(C + \gamma) = \alpha BC + \alpha B\gamma,$$

and

$$A\beta = A\beta C + A\beta\gamma;$$

hence, from (c), $\alpha B > A\beta$ implies $\alpha B\gamma > A\beta C$. So the number of fur coated spinsters with no operation is greater that the number of un-coated and de-appendicized married women.

EXERCISES

1. Let U be the set of university students in the United States. Let A be the set of university students in the United States who study mathematics, B be the set of university students who play football, and C be the set of honour students. Write down the positive and ultimate sets, and state in words the attributes of each set (for example, ABC is the set of honour university students studying mathematics who also play football).

2. Using the sets of Exercise 1, explain in words the meaning of the following mathematical statements:

   (a) $AB + AC = A + ABC - A\beta\gamma$,

   (b) $A\beta = A - AB$.

3. Draw Venn diagrams, marking in the frequencies of the positive and ultimate sets, for Examples 2.8.1 and 2.8.3.

4. Out of 1000 home-owners investigated, 560 owned their homes without a mortgage and also owned cars; 320 owned mortgaged houses, possessed cars, and had electricity; 189 owned houses but had neither cars nor electricity; 750 owned cars. Check these data for consistency.

5. In a certain government office there are 400 employees; there are 150 men, 276 university graduates, 212 married persons, 94 male university graduates, 151 married university graduates, 119 married men, 72 married male university graduates. Are these data consistent? If so, find the number of single women who are not university graduates.

6. On a certain bill, all 96 members of the United States Senate (before Hawaii and Alaska became states) were present and voted. The bill was passed by a majority of 18 and the following facts were noted: of the three Republican senators from the South, two voted against the bill; of the 23 Democratic senators from the South, only three voted against the bill; the bill was sponsored by the Democrats, but 19 senators bolted party lines on the vote. Finally, the number of non-southern Democrats voting for the bill was equal to the number of senators voting against the bill who were either southern Democrats or non-southern Republicans. Analyze the constitution of the senate.

3

Boolean Algebra

by Gerald Berman

3.1. INTRODUCTION

We shall commence with

Example 3.1.1. Consider a set I and two proper subsets X and Y as shown in the Venn diagram in Figure 3.1. It is clear that the pair X and Y partition I into four mutually exclusive subsets (Figure 3.2), namely, $A = X \cap Y$, $B = X' \cap Y$, $C = X \cap Y'$, and $D = X' \cap Y'$ (these sets A, B, C, and D are the ultimate sets of Section 2.7).

Assuming A, B, C, and D to be nonempty, we may form fifteen distinct nonempty sets by taking unions of A, B, C, and D. These are

$$A, B, C, D;$$

$$A \cup B, A \cup C, A \cup D, B \cup C, B \cup D, C \cup D;$$

$$A \cup B \cup C, A \cup B \cup D, A \cup C \cup D, B \cup C \cup D;$$

$$A \cup B \cup C \cup D = I.$$

Furthermore, every nonempty set that can be formed from X and Y by using the operations $\cap$, $\cup$, and $'$ can be expressed as a *union* of the sets A, B, C, and D, and hence is one of the fifteen sets. For example,

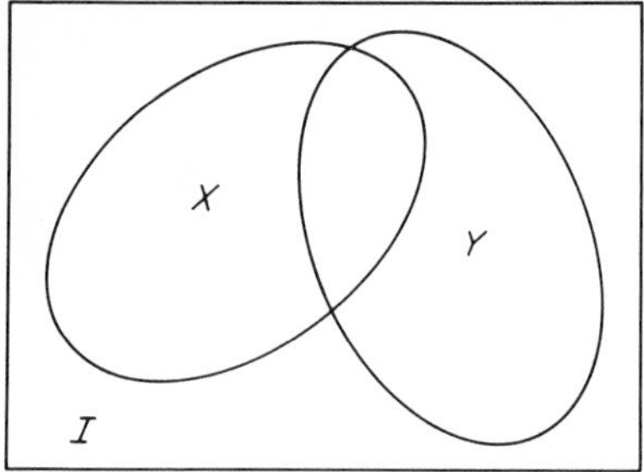

Figure 3.1

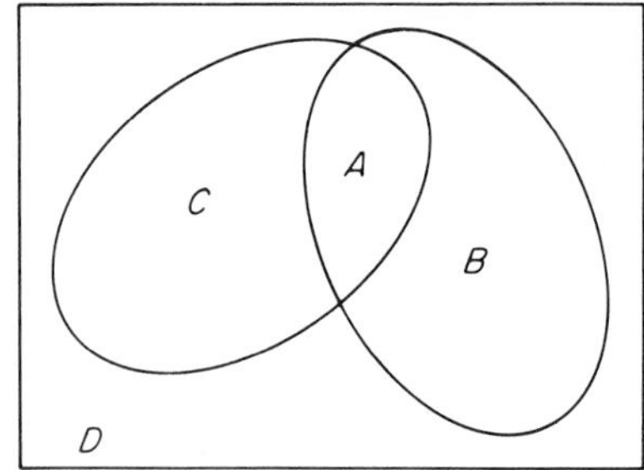

Figure 3.2

Example 3.1.2

$$\begin{aligned}(X' \cap Y) \cup X &= (X' \cup X) \cap (Y \cup X)\\ &= (Y \cup X)\\ &= [(X' \cup X) \cap Y] \cup [(Y' \cup Y) \cap X]\\ &= [(X' \cap Y) \cup (X \cap Y)] \cup [(Y' \cap X) \cup (Y \cap X)]\\ &= B \cup A \cup C \cup A\\ &= A \cup B \cup C.\end{aligned}$$

This collection of fifteen nonempty sets, together with the null set 0, is closed under the three operations of union $\cup$, intersection $\cap$, and complementation $'$; it is an example of a mathematical system called a Boolean Algebra. We shall now give an abstract definition of such a system.

A *Boolean Algebra* is a mathematical system consisting of a set B (with elements denoted by X, Y, etc.); two binary operations $\cup$ (union), $\cap$ (intersection); a binary relation $\leq$; and an operation $'$ (complementation) satisfying the following rules.

The binary operations $\cup$ and $\cap$ obey the idempotent, commutative, associative, and distributive laws, that is,

Idempotent Laws

(3.1.1) $$X \cap X = X; \qquad X \cup X = X;$$

Commutative Laws

(3.1.2) $$X \cap Y = Y \cap X; \qquad X \cup Y = Y \cup X;$$

Associative Laws

(3.1.3) $$\begin{aligned}X \cap (Y \cap Z) &= (X \cap Y) \cap Z;\\ X \cup (Y \cup Z) &= (X \cup Y) \cup Z;\end{aligned}$$

Distributive Laws

(3.1.4)
$$X \cap (Y \cup Z) = (X \cap Y) \cup (X \cap Z);$$
$$X \cup (Y \cap Z) = (X \cup Y) \cap (X \cup Z).$$

The binary relation $\leq$ is reflexive, antisymmetric, transitive, and satisfies the consistency principle, that is,

(3.1.5) *Reflexive Law* $X \leq X$.

(3.1.6) *Antisymmetric Law* If $X \leq Y$ and $Y \leq X$, then $X = Y$.

(3.1.7) *Transitive Law* If $X \leq Y$ and $Y \leq Z$, then $X \leq Z$.

(3.1.8) *Consistency Principle* The conditions (i) $X \leq Y$, (ii) $X \cap Y = X$, and (iii) $X \cup Y = Y$ are equivalent.

B contains elements 0 and I which are *universal bounds* and satisfy the intersection and union laws.

Universal Bounds

(3.1.9)
$$0 \leq X \leq I.$$

Intersection Laws

(3.1.10)
$$0 \cap X = 0; \qquad I \cap X = X.$$

Union Laws

(3.1.11)
$$0 \cup X = X; \qquad I \cup X = I.$$

The unary operation $'$, called *complementation*, obeys the complementarity, dualization, and involution laws.

Complementarity Laws

(3.1.12)
$$X \cap X' = 0; \qquad X \cup X' = I.$$

Dualization Laws

(3.1.13)
$$(X \cap Y)' = X' \cup Y'; \qquad (X \cup Y)' = X' \cap Y'.$$

Involution Law

(3.1.14)
$$(X')' = X.$$

An examination of the definition indicates that a Boolean Algebra is not only a very abstract entity, but also is quite complicated!

It can easily be verified that the collection of sixteen sets described in Example 3.1.1 does indeed form a Boolean Algebra. In fact, closure under the various operations has already been discussed, and the rules are just the rules which we know (cf. Chapter 2) hold for any sets.

Examples of Boolean Algebras are much simpler to understand than the abstract system; however, it can frequently be presented in terms of elementary ideas and concrete objects, just as in Example 3.1.1. In this chapter, we shall try to present further examples and to indicate the application of Boolean Algebra to other disciplines, in particular, to logic and circuit theory.

3.2. CONNECTION WITH SET THEORY

It was pointed out in Chapter 2 that the various rules (3.1.1) to (3.1.14) for a Boolean Algebra hold for the collection of all subsets of a set where $\cup$ and $\cap$ are interpreted as the union and intersection of sets, where $\leq$ is interpreted as inclusion, where $'$ is interpreted as complementation of a set, and where I is the universe U. Thus, *the set of all subsets of a given set* U is a second example of a Boolean Algebra.

Example 3.1.3. Consider the set

$$U = \{1, 2, 3, 4, 5, 6, 7\};$$

there are $2^7 = 128$ possible subsets of U (including the empty set), and these subsets form a Boolean Algebra.

Example 3.1.4. Let I represent all points in or on the square with vertices at (0, 0), (0, 5), (5, 0), (5, 5). Let X represent the set of all points in or on the circle with radius 1 and center (2, 2); let Y represent the set of all points in or on the circle with radius 1 and center (3, 2).

The fifteen sets formed from

$$X \cap Y, \quad X \cap Y', \quad X' \cap Y, \quad X' \cap Y',$$

together with the null set, form a Boolean Algebra (Example 3.1.1). So does the collection of *all* subsets of I (Example 3.1.4); note that the collection of all subsets of I is infinite.

Before going any further it might be well to point out (without proof) a fundamental theorem concerning Boolean Algebras.

THEOREM. *Every Boolean Algebra is isomorphic to a Boolean Algebra of subsets of a set.*

This theorem shows that every Boolean Algebra is equivalent to a Boolean Algebra like those of the Examples 3.1.1, 3.1.3, and 3.1.4. Consequently, we really did not need to define a Boolean Algebra in quite such an abstract manner; indeed, we could merely have talked about an "algebra of subsets" without glorifying the "algebra of subsets" with the name Boolean Algebra.

3.3. CONNECTION WITH LOGIC

We will now give an example to illustrate how the idea of a Boolean Algebra is related to logic.

Example 3.1.5. Let us take a very special set I, the mathematics teachers in the Province of Ontario. Consider some "declaratory statements" about this set I (we shall use P to denote an element of I).

$S(0)$: P is 127 years old.

$S(1)$: P is interested in mathematics.

$S(2)$: P has a pleasant personality.

$S(X)$: P is less than 5′10″ in height.

$S(Y)$: P has blue eyes.

Everyone will agree that $S(0)$ is not true for any person P in I. We will agree that statement $S(1)$ is valid for all members of I. The statement $S(2)$ is not as clear-cut; there might easily be some disagreement in deciding on the validity of $S(2)$ when applied to some particular persons (the authors, for example). This point suggests the need for some means of judging the validity of a statement. Once agreement has been reached on certain statements, the validity of certain others is a consequence. Let us suppose it has been agreed which of the statements $S(0)$, $S(1)$, $S(X)$, $S(Y)$, are valid for any particular person in I. Then, to each statement there corresponds a subset of I consisting of all persons in I for which the statement is true.

The statements $S(0)$ and $S(1)$ correspond to the sets 0 and I respectively. Let $S(X)$ and $S(Y)$ correspond to subsets X and Y of I. The sets $X \cap Y$, $X \cup Y$, and X' then correspond to the following statements.

$S(X \cap Y)$: P is less than 5′10″ in height *and* has blue eyes.

$S(X \cup Y)$: Either P is less than 5′10″ in height *or* P has blue eyes.

$S(X')$: P is *not* less than 5′10″ in height.

The sets $X \cap Y$, $X \cup Y$, and X' are well defined. There are sixteen different sets (cf. Example 3.1.1). Each of these sets corresponds to some derived statement.

Two statements $S(A)$ and $S(B)$ about the elements of I are called *equivalent* if they correspond to the same subset (that is, if $A = B$). Using the Boolean Algebra of sets, the equivalence of logical statements is easily checked. For example, it was shown earlier that

$$(X' \cap Y) \cup X = X \cup Y = (X \cap Y) \cup (X' \cap Y) \cup (X \cap Y').$$

This implies the equivalence of the following two statements.

$S[(X' \cap Y) \cup X]$: P is not shorter than 5′10″ and has blue eyes, or P is less than 5′10″ in height.

$S(X \cup Y)$: Either P is less than 5′10″ in height or P has blue eyes.

The equivalent statement $S[(X \cap Y) \cup (X' \cap Y) \cup (X \cap Y')]$ is also easily put into words. Complicated statements may sometimes be simplified in this way by using the corresponding Boolean Algebra.

Example 3.1.5 has illustrated the exact one-to-one correspondence between the algebra of statements involving $S(0)$, $S(1)$, $S(X)$, $S(Y)$, and the Boolean Algebra of sets we constructed in Example 3.1.1. Notice that $=$, $\cup$, $\cap$, $'$, in the Boolean Algebra of Example 3.1.1 correspond to "is equivalent to", "or", "and", and "not", respectively, in the algebra of statements in Example 3.1.5. This correspondence may be used to construct another example of a Boolean Algebra which occurs in a natural setting.

Let B be the set of all declaratory statements (sometimes called assertions or propositions) about elements of a parent universe I. Thus, in Example 3.1.5, we would increase our collection of statements from merely sixteen statements that can be formed from $S(0)$, $S(1)$, $S(X)$, $S(Y)$, to the infinite collection of all possible statements about elements of I. Compound statements may be constructed from these statements by using the connectives $\cap$, $\cup$, and $'$, as described in Example 3.1.5. It is easy to verify that all the rules for a Boolean Algebra hold. For example, $X \cup Y = Y \cup X$, since the statement "Either X or Y is true" has the same meaning as (is equivalent to) "Either Y or X is true". Notice that I can be taken as any true statement, and 0 as any false statement. Thus, we have exemplified the

THEOREM. *The Algebra of Statements under the connectives "and", "or", and "not" is a Boolean Algebra.*

The ideas of logic will be further discussed in Chapter 4.

3.4. SWITCHING NETWORKS

We will now illustrate how the ideas that we have been discussing can be applied in Electrical Engineering to the theory of switching networks and in the construction of computers.

An ordinary switch has two states, "open" and "closed" (Figure 3.3). A closed switch permits the passage of current, and an open switch does not. A switching network is an arrangement of switches with wires connecting

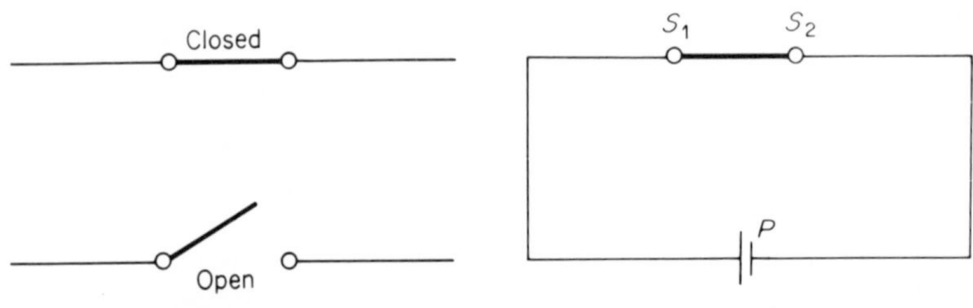

Figure 3.3

Fig. 3.4 Network N_1

them. The simplest switching networks containing two switches S_1 and S_2 are shown in Figures 3.4 and 3.5. In each case, P is a source of power. In the network N_1 of Figure 3.4, the switches are connected in *series*; the current will flow only when *both* switches are closed. Thus the series arrangement

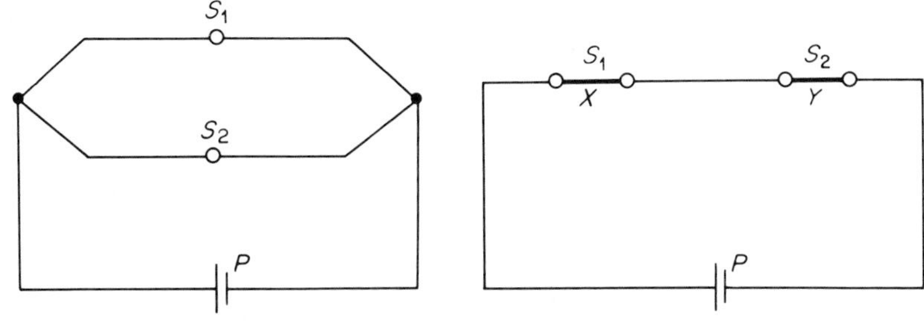

Fig. 3.5 Network N_2 **Fig. 3.6** $X \cap Y$

corresponds to the logical operation $\cap$. If the states of the switches are denoted by X, X' (X closed, X' open), and Y, Y' (Y closed, Y' open), Figures 3.6 and 3.7 illustrate the states of network N_1 corresponding to $X \cap Y$ and $X' \cap Y$.

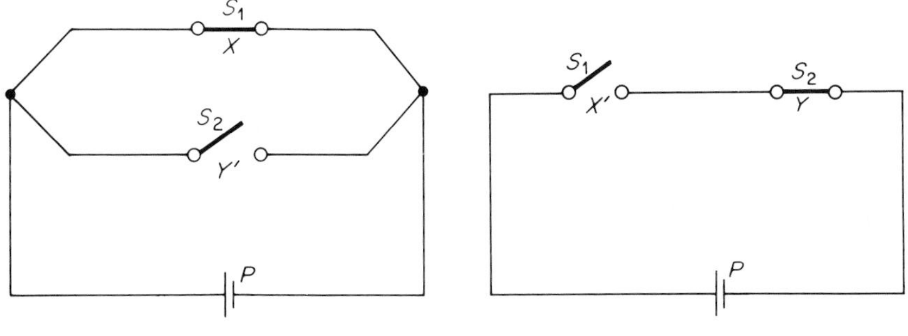

Fig. 3.7 $X' \cap Y$ **Fig. 3.8** $X \cup Y'$

Similarly, the network N_2 of Figure 3.5, consisting of two switches connected in parallel, corresponds to the logical operation $\cup$, since current will flow if *either* of the switches is closed. This correspondence is illustrated in Figures 3.8 and 3.9.

More complicated switching networks can be built up by using *multiple switches*. In the switches already discussed, the operation of a single external lever controls the current in a single wire. In a multiple switch, one lever simultaneously controls the flow of current in several wires. Consider the diagram shown in Figure 3.10. Three wires are connected to a multiple switch $ABCDH$. The connection AB is hinged at H, and the operation of a mechanical lever joins either CD or AB (AB is joined in Figure 3.10). In the position shown in Figure 3.10, current is flowing through wires W_1 and W_2, but not through W_3. If the lever is operated, the current will flow through W_3 but not through W_1 and W_2. The situation is more easily

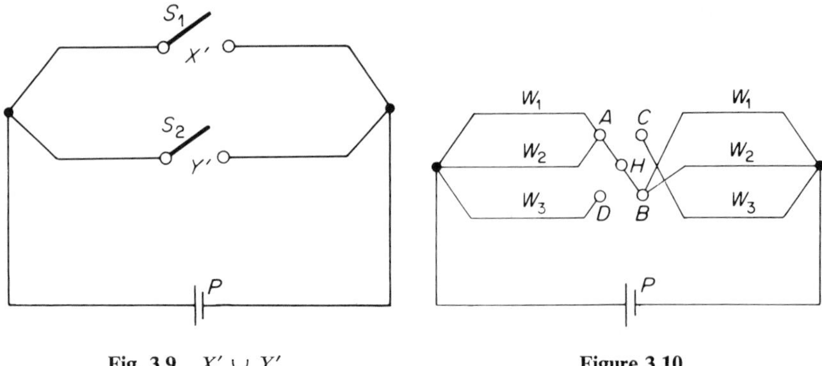

Fig. 3.9 $X' \cup Y'$

Figure 3.10

represented schematically by the diagram shown in Figure 3.11; in this diagram the multiple switch is represented by three single switches (one on each wire) which are simultaneously operated by a single lever. The closed

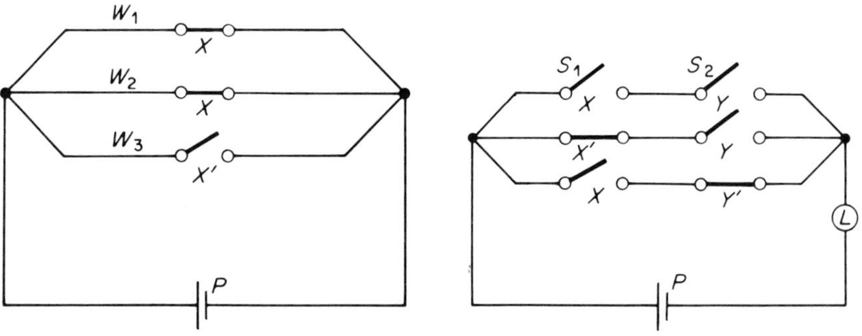

Figure 3.11

Fig. 3.12 $(X \cap Y) \cup (X' \cap Y) \cup (X \cap Y')$

state is designated by X, and the open by X'. If the lever is moved, X will become X' and X' will become X. The states of a second switch might be designated by Y and Y', etc.

The situation can easily be generalized. As an example of a switching network involving two multiple switches, consider the arrangement of Figure 3.12 (we have used X, Y to denote open switches in this case). P is a power source, and L is a light bulb. Throwing switch S_1 interchanges the states X and X', whereas throwing S_2 interchanges Y and Y'. An examination shows that throwing *either* switch will allow current to flow and light the

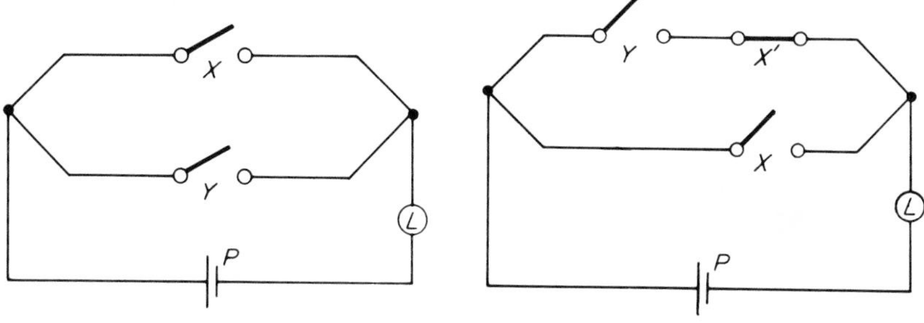

Fig. 3.13 $X \cup Y$ **Fig. 3.14** $(X' \cap Y) \cup X$

bulb L. Thus, the arrangement of Figure 3.13 (network N_2) will provide an equivalent situation.

The equivalence of the networks in Figures 3.12 and 3.13 is easily demonstrated using Boolean Algebra. The first arrangement corresponds to the logical statement $(X \cap Y) \cup (X' \cap Y) \cup (X \cap Y')$ and the second arrangement to $X \cup Y$; but we have already shown these two statements to be equivalent (cf. Example 3.1.2). Since $X \cup Y$ was shown to be equivalent to $(X' \cap Y) \cup X$ in the same example, a third possible network representing "OR" could be constructed, as in Figure 3.14. In this way, Boolean Algebra may be used to show the equivalence of switching networks and also to construct networks which represent a given logical relation.

Example 3.4.1. Construct a switching network for a light in a stairway with two switches (one upstairs, one downstairs).

An examination of the situation suggests that the logical statement $(X \cap Y) \cup (X' \cap Y')$ corresponds to the required network; for the light is to be on if the switches are both in the states X and Y or both in the states X' and Y'; otherwise, the light is to be off. The diagram corresponding to the switching network is given in Figure 3.15. It is easily seen that the network has the required properties. Figure 3.16 illustrates an alternative network.

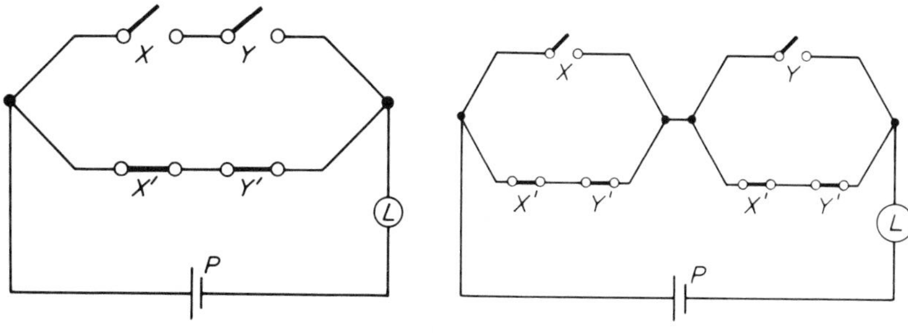

Figure 3.15 **Figure 3.16**

3.5. BLACK BOXES

The application of Boolean Algebra to computers is more sophisticated. In the early days of the modern computer, remote control switches were used as basic components. Now, vacuum tubes, transistors, and other such electrical components have taken their place.

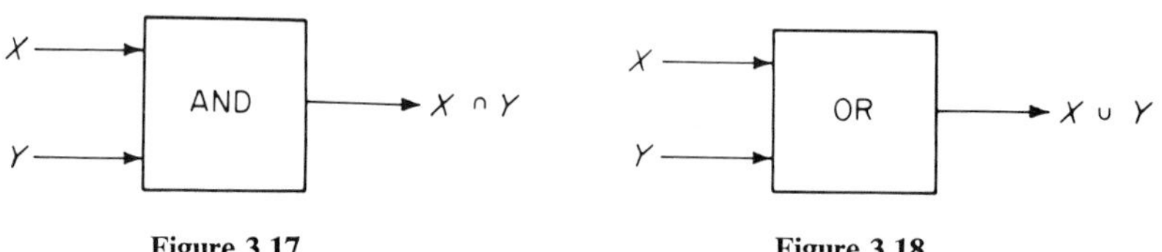

Figure 3.17 Figure 3.18

In this application, the logical connectives "and", "or", and "not", correspond to subnetworks, sometimes called "black boxes", and the X, Y, etc., correspond to different electrical (input) pulses.

The black box AND has two inputs and one output. It is constructed in such a way that there is an output pulse only if there are *two* input pulses (Figure 3.17). Similarly, the OR box has two inputs and one output, but this time there is an output pulse if *either* one of the inputs contains an electrical impulse. The NOT box has one input and one output; it is constructed to give an output pulse if and only if there is no input pulse. Thus, the AND, OR, and NOT boxes correspond to the logical operations $\cap$, $\cup$, and $'$, which we have been considering. We shall not discuss how these boxes are constructed; suffice it to say that they may be constructed in many ways.

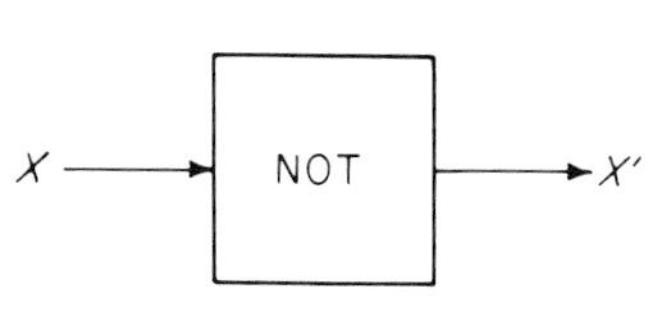

Figure 3.19

A network may be constructed corresponding to any combination of logical operations. For example, the output of the following network

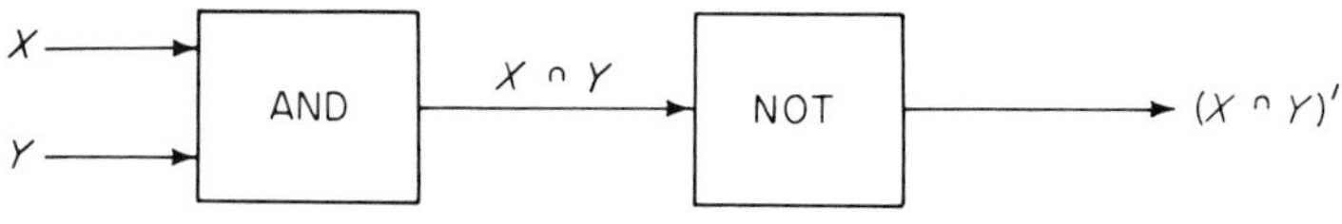

Figure 3.20

(Figure 3.20) is $(X \cap Y)'$. The network corresponding to the equivalent logical statement $X' \cup Y'$ is given in Figure 3.21. More complicated networks are easily constructed. Consider our old friend $(X \cap Y) \cup (X' \cap Y) \cup (X \cap Y')$. Although the corresponding network looks complicated, it is quite simple to construct (on paper, anyway!); cf. Figure 3.22. From our

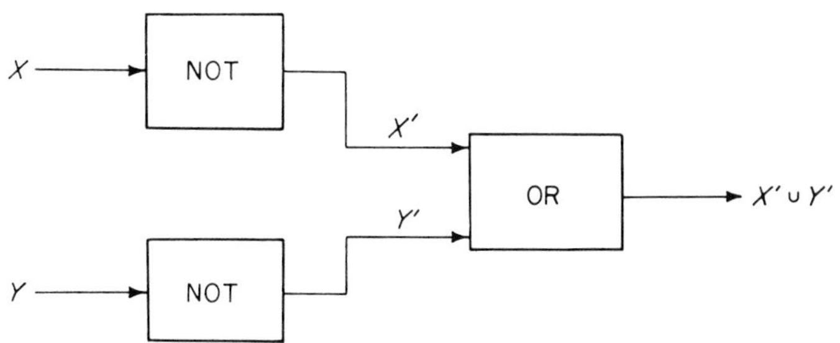

Figure 3.21

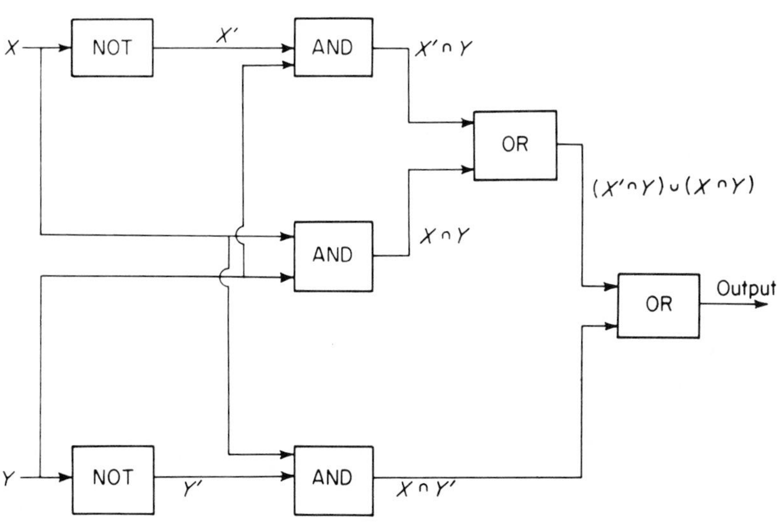

Fig. 3.22 $(X' \cap Y) \cup (X \cap Y') \cup (X \cap Y)$

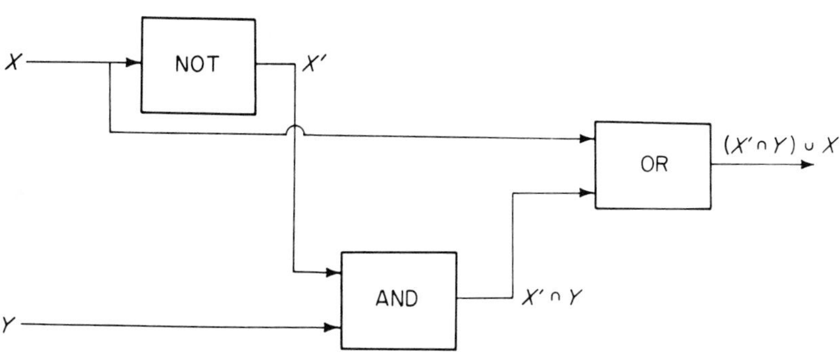

Fig. 3.23 $(X' \cap Y) \cup X$

previous remarks, it is clear that this complicated network is equivalent to the simple box OR, and we have a third equivalent network corresponding to $(X' \cap Y) \cup X$ given in Figure 3.23.

EXERCISE

1. Show that the following networks correspond to solutions of the "hall-light problem". Note that the second network uses fewer boxes.

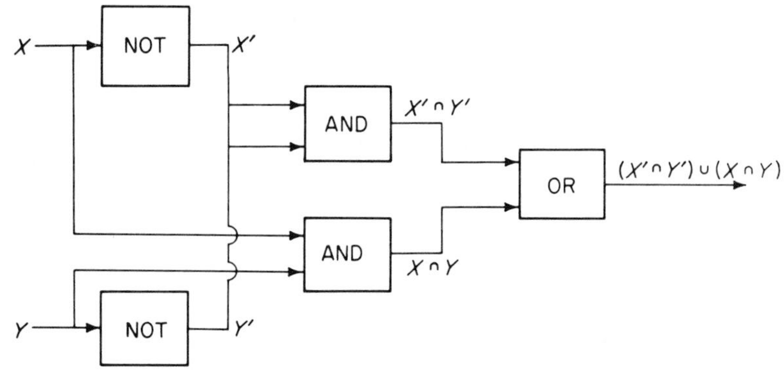

Fig. 3.24 $(X' \cap Y') \cup (X \cap Y)$

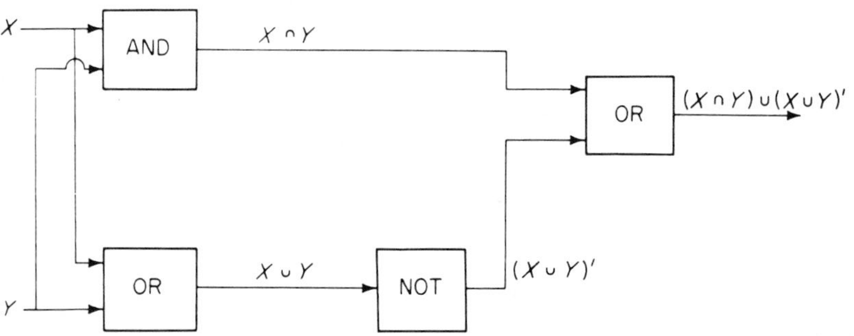

Fig. 3.25 $(X \cap Y) \cup (X \cup Y)'$

3.6. CONCLUDING REMARKS

We have covered a number of ideas quite rapidly, and a complete understanding of them would naturally require further time. Our main purpose has been to present a bird's-eye view of the subject. Although the background ideas involved are abstract and complex, important and interesting applications are available when one enters a specific technical field.

4

Logic and Computing

by Ralph G. Stanton

4.1. THE ALGEBRA OF LOGIC

This chapter will deal specifically with the symbolic approach to statements. In this connection, perhaps we should commence by making a distinction between *logic* and "*logic*".

Logic, according to the *Concise Oxford Dictionary*, is the "Science of reasoning, proof, thinking, or inference; chain of reasoning; use of argument", et cetera. Roughly, we can say that logic is akin to common sense. Indeed, logic in the sense of "chain of reasoning, use of argument" has been used in mathematics for countless centuries. We shall give some illustrations of good mathematical logic in Section 4.5.

"*Logic*" has come into use relatively recently; we shall use it to denote symbolic logic, the replacing of English by symbols and squiggles, the translation of English statements into what is really a foreign language. Now there are perfectly sound reasons for such an approach at very specialized levels in certain corners of advanced mathematics; no one should object if any specialist needs a special jargon. On the other hand, we may legitimately question whether a secondary school student will benefit from knowing that if p represents the statement "The book is red", then $\sim p$ represents the statement "The book is not red". I can recall a mathematical colloquium where, after two lines had been written on the blackboard, a famous contemporary mathematician rose and irately asked the speaker: "What is the use of your writing all these symbols on the board, when the first thing you have to do is translate them back into English?"

The three basic signs of elementary symbolic logic are the signs $\cap$, $\cup$, $\sim$, which represent conjunction of two statements (both-and), disjunction of two statements (either-or), and negation of a statement (not), respectively. Thus, if p and q represent two statements, we have:

$$p \cap q \quad (\text{both } p \text{ and } q),$$

$$p \cup q \quad (\text{either } p \text{ or } q),$$

$$\sim p \quad (\text{not } p).$$

Example 4.1.1. For illustration, let us consider the statements:

$$p = \text{Every triangle is equilateral,}$$

$$q = \text{The sum of two odd numbers is even.}$$

Notice that a statement is merely a declaratory sentence; it may be true (as q is here) or false (as p is here). Then we can form compound statements:

$p \cap q =$ Every triangle is equilateral, *and* the sum of two odd numbers is even;
$p \cup q =$ Every triangle is equilateral, *or* the sum of two odd numbers is even;
$\sim p =$ Not every triangle is equilateral;
$\sim q =$ The sum of two odd numbers is not even (that is, the sum is odd).

Note that p is false and hence $\sim p$ (not p) is true; we could make an error in negating p if we misplaced the "not" and thought that the negation of p was "Every triangle is not equilateral" (here we would be negating the adjective "equilateral", but not the whole statement).

Example 4.1.2. A recent text considers the statements:

$$p = \text{The night is young,}$$

$$q = \text{You are beautiful.}$$

Translate $(\sim p \cap q) \cup (p \cap \sim q)$.

The reader may readily verify that the answer is "Either the night is not young and you are beautiful, *or* the night is young and you are not beautiful". In either case, an alternative conclusion could easily be reached, namely, "We might as well go home!"

EXERCISES

1. Let p = Side AB of triangle ABC is 6 units long,
   q = Side BC of triangle ABC is 3 units long,
   r = Angle ABC of triangle ABC is 60°.

   Translate the following statements:

   (a) $\sim q$, (b) $p \cap r$, (c) $p \cup q$,
   (d) $\sim p \cup r$, (e) $\sim(p \cup r)$, (f) $p \cap \sim q$,
   (g) $(p \cup r) \cap q$, (h) $p \cup (r \cap q)$, (i) $\sim[p \cup q \cup r]$,
   (j) $(\sim p \cup q) \cap \sim r$, (k) $(\sim p \cap q) \cup (p \cap \sim r) \cup (\sim q \cap \sim r)$.

2. Let p = The number $\sqrt{2}$ is a rational number,
   q = The number π is an integer.

   Translate the following statements:

   (a) $\sim p$, (b) $p \cup q$,
   (c) $p \cap q$, (d) $\sim p \cup q$,
   (e) $\sim(p \cup q)$, (f) $\sim p \cap \sim q$,
   (g) $(\sim p \cup \sim q) \cup (p \cap \sim q)$, (h) $[(p \cup q) \cup (\sim p \cup q)] \cap p$.

4.2. TRUTH TABLES

In the preceding section, we considered how statements could be put together to form new compound statements; we did not consider whether the original statements or the resulting compound statements were true or false. Now we shall think about whether a statement p is true (in which case we label p with the letter T) or false (in which case we label p with the letter F); naturally, the compound statements involving p can likewise be labelled T or F. The result can be presented in the form of a *truth table*.

Since any statement can be labelled either T or F, there will be four possibilities in compound statements involving two original statements, eight possibilities in compound statements involving three original statements, and, in general, 2^n possibilities in compound statements involving n original statements.

Example 4.2.1. *Truth Table for Negation*

p	T	F
$\sim p$	F	T

This table simply states that if p is true, then $\sim p$ is false; whereas if p is false, then $\sim p$ is true.

Example 4.2.2. *Truth Table for Conjunction*

p q	T T	T F	F T	F F
$p \cap q$	T	F	F	F

The first two lines of this truth table give the four possibilities when only two statements are involved; they will be the same for all tables involving just two statements p and q. The third line labels $p \cap q$ as true (T) only in that case when both p and q are true. Similarly, the truth table for disjunction would have the same first two lines, but would have a third line

$p \cup q$	T	T	T	F

This result indicates that $p \cup q$ is true (T) whenever either p or q is labelled T (thus $p \cup q$ is labelled F only when both p and q are labelled F).

A more complicated table can always be built up if needed; let us consider

Example 4.2.3. Evaluate the truth of the statement $(\sim p \cap q) \cup (p \cap \sim q)$ in terms of the truth values of p and q.

The solution involves building up successively truth values for the following required combinations.

p, q: four initial possibilities;

$\sim p, \sim q$: the *negations* of p and q;

$\sim p \cap q, p \cap \sim q$: *conjunction* of known statements;

$(\sim p \cap q) \cup (p \cap \sim q)$: *disjunction* of the two preceding statements.

The complete table follows.

p q	T T	T F	F T	F F
$\sim p$	F	F	T	T
$\sim q$	F	T	F	T
$\sim p \cap q$	F	F	T	F
$p \cap \sim q$	F	T	F	F
$(\sim p \cap q) \cup (p \cap \sim q)$	F	T	T	F

It follows that the compound statement $(\sim p \cap q) \cup (p \cap \sim q)$ is true if and only if exactly one of p and q is true.

EXERCISES

1. Build up truth tables for the statements:
   (a) $(p \cap \sim q \cap \sim r) \cup (\sim p \cup \sim q \cup r)$,
   (b) $[p \cap (q \cup \sim r)] \cap [\sim p \cup (\sim q \cap r)]$,
   (c) $[p \cap \sim q] \cup [q \cap \sim r] \cup [p \cup (\sim q \cap \sim r)]$.
2. Build up truth tables for
   (a) $[(p \cup \sim q) \cap (q \cup r \cup s)] \cup (\sim p \cap \sim s)$,
   (b) $(p \cup \sim s) \cup (q \cap \sim r \cap \sim s) \cup (p \cup \sim r \cup s) \cup (\sim r \cap \sim s)$.
3. Let p = The number π is an integer,
   q = The number $\sqrt{25}$ is an integer,
   r = The number $\frac{143}{12}$ is an integer.

   Which column of the truth table in Exercise 1(a) is relevant to this problem? Is the statement

   $$(p \cap \sim q \cap \sim r) \cup (\sim p \cup \sim q \cup r)$$

   true or false? Write out this compound statement in words (why would anyone make such a compound statement?).
4. Make truth tables for the following statements:
   (a) $p \cap (q \cup r)$, (b) $(p \cap q) \cup r$,
   (c) $(\sim p \cup q) \cap \sim r$, (d) $\sim p \cup (q \cap \sim r)$.

   Which columns of each table are relevant to the three statements of Exercise 3?

4.3. IMPLICATION AND EQUIVALENCE

Let us begin with two illustrations.

Example 4.3.1.

p = The two integers a and b are odd.

q = The sum of two integers a and b is an even integer $a + b$.

Whenever p is true, then q is true. So we say that "p implies q", and use a double arrow to write symbolically

$$p \Rightarrow q.$$

Note that implication is a one-way relation; $p \Rightarrow q$ does not automatically produce a true converse statement. Indeed, in this example, the converse statement $q \Rightarrow p$ is not a true statement (since, if the sum of two integers is an even integer $a + b$, it does *not* necessarily follow that a and b are both odd integers).

Example 4.3.2.

$p = \triangle ABC$ has three equal sides.

$q = \triangle ABC$ has three equal angles.

Here, $p \Rightarrow q$, and conversely $q \Rightarrow p$; in such a case, we say that the two statements are *equivalent*, and write

$$p \Leftrightarrow q.$$

The statement $p \Leftrightarrow q$ can be read in many ways. We may read:

"p is equivalent to q";
or "p implies q, and q implies p";
or "p implies and is implied by q";
or "the truth of p is a necessary and sufficient condition for the truth of q";
or "if p is true, q is true; and, if p is false, q is false";
or "p is true if and only if q is true".

Note that "p is true if q is true" is the statement $q \Rightarrow p$, whereas "p is true only if q is true" is the statement $p \Rightarrow q$. Note also that "the truth of p is a necessary condition for the truth of q" is the statement $q \Rightarrow p$; whereas "the truth of p is a sufficient condition for the truth of q" is the statement $p \Rightarrow q$. Beginning students often find the phraseology of "if and only if" or "a necessary and sufficient condition" difficult, and it is desirable that they should state $p \Rightarrow q$ and $q \Rightarrow p$ in the form of two theorems rather than attempt to join them in "one" theorem.

EXERCISES

1. Let $p = \triangle ABC$ and $\triangle DEF$ are congruent,
   $q = [AB = DE, BC = EF, CA = FD]$.
   Which of the following statements are true?
   (a) $p \Rightarrow q$, (b) $q \Rightarrow p$, (c) $p \Leftrightarrow q$.
2. Let $p = \triangle ABC$ and $\triangle DEF$ are similar,
   $q = (AB = DE)$,
   $r = (\angle ABC = \angle DEF, \angle ACB = \angle DFE)$.
   Which of the following are true?
   (a) $(p \Rightarrow q) \cup (q \Rightarrow p)$, (b) $(p \Rightarrow r) \cup (q \Rightarrow r)$,
   (c) $(r \Rightarrow p) \cap (p \Rightarrow r)$, (d) $(r \Rightarrow p) \cup (q \Rightarrow p)$,
   (e) $(p \Rightarrow q) \cup (q \Rightarrow r) \cup (r \Rightarrow p) \cup (q \Rightarrow r)$.
3. Let $p = \triangle ABC$ is right-angled at B,
   $q = [AB^2 + BC^2 = AC^2]$,
   $r = (AC \geq AB)$.

Which of the following are true?

(a) $p \Rightarrow q$, (b) $q \Rightarrow p$,
(c) $p \Leftrightarrow q$, (d) $p \Rightarrow r$,
(e) $r \Rightarrow p$, (f) $p \Leftrightarrow r$,
(g) $q \Rightarrow r$, (h) $r \Rightarrow q$,
(i) $q \Leftrightarrow r$, (j) $p \Rightarrow (q \cap r)$,
(k) $(p \cup q) \Rightarrow r$, (l) $(r \cup \sim p) \Rightarrow q$,
(m) $\sim q \Rightarrow \sim r$, (n) $(p \Rightarrow r) \Rightarrow (q \Rightarrow r)$,
(o) $(p \Rightarrow r) \cup (r \Rightarrow q)$.

4. Consider the following statements.
   p = A, B, and C are distinct points on the circumference of a circle,
   q = ACB is a right angle,
   r = AB is a diameter.

   Write out the following statements and label them true or false.

   (a) $p \cap r \Rightarrow q$, (b) $p \cap q \Rightarrow r$, (c) $p \cap r \Leftrightarrow p \cap q$.

5. The following statements are given.
   p = Angle ABC equals angle ADC ($B \neq D$, B and D on the same side of AC),
   q = Points $ABCD$ are concyclic,
   r = Angle ABC and angle ADC are supplementary.

   Express the following theorems in symbolic form.

   (a) If a line AC subtends equal angles at two points B and D, then the four points are concyclic (B and D on the same side of AC).
   (b) If $ABCD$ is a cyclic quadrilateral, then the angles subtended by AD at the points B and C are either equal or supplementary.

6. Consider the following statements about a triangle ABC with D on the side BC and E on the side AC.

$$p = DE \text{ is parallel to } AB.$$

$$q = [AE/EC = BD/DC].$$

   Write in symbolic form the following theorems.

   (a) A necessary condition for DE to be parallel to AB is that $AE/EC = BD/DC$.
   (b) A sufficient condition for DE to be parallel to AB is that $AE/EC = BD/DC$.
   (c) $AE/EC = BD/DC$ only if DE is parallel to AB.
   (d) $AE/EC = BD/DC$ if DE is parallel to AB.

4.4. TAUTOLOGIES

In the last sections, we gained some practice in attaching truth values to compound statements. It turns out that some statements are true regardless of the truth or falsehood of the component statements; such compound statements are called *tautologies*.

Example 4.4.1.

The statement $p \cup (\sim p)$ is a tautology.

To prove this result by using a truth table, we form

p	T	F
$\sim p$	F	T
$p \cup (\sim p)$	T	T

The truth table has all T's on the last line; thus, we are dealing with an always-true statement, that is, a tautology. In this case, the tautology is known as the *Law of the Excluded Middle* and can be phrased in words as "Either the statement p is true or the negated statement $\sim p$ is true".

There are various other important tautologies which have been used in logical reasoning for a very long time (long before they were put in symbolic form). We shall work them out as examples.

Example 4.4.2.

The statement $\sim [p \cap (\sim p)]$ is a tautology.

The requisite truth table is simply

p	T	F
$\sim p$	F	T
$p \cap (\sim p)$	F	F
$\sim [p \cap (\sim p)]$	T	T

Again we have the statement true irrespective of whatever statement p is. This tautology, which is known as the *Law of Contradiction*, may be phrased in words as "It is impossible for the statement p and the contradictory statement $\sim p$ both to be true".

Example 4.4.3.

$$[(p \Rightarrow q) \cap (q \Rightarrow r)] \Rightarrow (p \Rightarrow r).$$

This particular implication, known as the *Law of the Syllogism*, is well known in words: If p implies q, and q implies r, then p implies r. For instance, if

$p = ABC$ is a triangle, right-angled at B;

$$q = [AB^2 + BC^2 = AC^2];$$

$$r = (AC \geq AB);$$

we know that $p \Rightarrow q$, and we know that $q \Rightarrow r$; hence $p \Rightarrow r$.

One of the oldest examples of a syllogism occurs for the statements

$$p = A \text{ is Socrates,}$$

$$q = A \text{ is a man,}$$

$$r = A \text{ is mortal.}$$

Then

$$p \Rightarrow q = \text{Socrates is a man,}$$

$$q \Rightarrow r = \text{All men are mortal.}$$

It follows that

$$p \Rightarrow r, \quad \text{that is, Socrates is mortal.}$$

Example 4.4.4. The very important result

$$(p \Rightarrow q) \Leftrightarrow [(\sim q) \Rightarrow (\sim p)],$$

known as the *Law of the Contrapositive*, is slightly more troublesome. So we give a complete proof.

Suppose $p \Rightarrow q$ and that $\sim q$ is given; then we may conclude

$$p \cup (\sim p)$$

by the Law of the Excluded Middle; thus, we have two possibilities: p or $\sim p$. But we can not have p, since that would imply q, and then we should have $q \cap \sim q$, which is impossible. Hence, $\sim p$. So we have $\sim q \Rightarrow \sim p$.

Conversely, suppose $\sim q \Rightarrow \sim p$, and that p is given. Then we have q or $\sim q$. If $\sim q$, then $\sim p$, by hypothesis; this results in the contradiction $p \cap \sim p$. Hence we must have q, that is, $p \Rightarrow q$.

It is instructive to apply this result to an illustration.

Example 4.4.4(a)

$p =$ The two integers a and b are odd.

$q =$ The sum $a + b$ of the two integers a and b is even.

Certainly $p \Rightarrow q$ and $\sim q \Rightarrow \sim p$ are equivalent statements, namely,

$p \Rightarrow q$: If a and b are odd integers, then their sum $a + b$ is even.

$\sim q \Rightarrow \sim p$: If the sum of two integers is not even, then the integers are not both odd.

Notice particularly that $p \Rightarrow q$ is not equivalent to $\sim p \Rightarrow \sim q$; this latter statement would read:

If "a and b odd" is false (that is, if at least one of them is even), then their sum is not even.

But this statement is clearly false.

Another example of the use of the contrapositive would be

Example 4.4.4(b)

$$p = \triangle\text{'s } ABC \text{ and } DEF \text{ are congruent.}$$

$$q = \triangle\text{'s } ABC \text{ and } DEF \text{ are similar.}$$

Here $p \Rightarrow q$ (since two congruent triangles are similar); the equivalent statement $\sim q \Rightarrow \sim p$ would be: If two triangles are not similar, they are not congruent.

Finally,

Example 4.4.4(c)

$$p = \text{The angle } x \text{ is equal to } 90°.$$

$$q = \text{The sine of } x \text{ is equal to } 1.$$

Then $p \Rightarrow q$ (since $\sin 90° = 1$); the statement $\sim q \Rightarrow \sim p$ reads: If $\sin x \neq 1$, then x can not equal $90°$.

Clearly these statements are equivalent.

Example 4.4.5. It is obvious, either verbally or from a truth table, that

$$p \Leftrightarrow \sim(\sim p).$$

This result is known as the *Law of Double Negation*; in words, the negation of the negation of p is p.

Example 4.4.6. Prove the tautology

$$p \cap (q \cup r) \Leftrightarrow (p \cap q) \cup (p \cap r).$$

Make a truth table as follows.

p	T	T	T	T	F	F	F	F
q	T	F	T	F	T	F	T	F
r	T	T	F	F	T	T	F	F
$p \cap q$	T	F	T	F	F	F	F	F
$p \cap r$	T	T	F	F	F	F	F	F
$(p \cap q) \cup (p \cap r)$	T	T	T	F	F	F	F	F
$q \cup r$	T	T	T	F	T	T	T	F
$p \cap (q \cup r)$	T	T	T	F	F	F	F	F

The result shows up clearly in the complete equivalence of rows 6 and 8 of the truth table; since $(p \cap q) \cup (p \cap r)$ is true whenever $p \cap (q \cup r)$ is true, and false whenever $p \cap (q \cup r)$ is false, the equivalence of the two expressions is a tautology.

EXERCISES

1. Make a truth table to establish the tautology:

$$p \cup (q \cap r) \Leftrightarrow (p \cup q) \cap (p \cup r).$$

2. Use a truth table to discuss the expressions

$$p \cup q \quad \text{and} \quad (p \cap q) \cup (p \cap \sim q) \cup (\sim p \cap q).$$

3. Use a truth table to show that

(a) $p \cap q \Leftrightarrow \sim [(p \cap \sim q) \cup (\sim p \cap \sim q) \cup (\sim p \cap q)]$,
(b) $(p \cap \sim q) \cup (\sim p \cap q) \Leftrightarrow \sim [(p \cap q) \cup (\sim p \cap \sim q)]$.

4. Does $\sim p \Rightarrow \sim q$ in Examples 4.4.4(b) and 4.4.4(c)?

5. Consider the following statements:

$$p = x, y, \text{ and } z \text{ are real numbers such that}$$
$$x^2 + y^2 + z^2 + 2(xy + yz + zx) = 0,$$
$$q = [x + y + z = 0],$$
$$r = [x^3 + y^3 + z^3 = 3xyz].$$

Use this result to illustrate a syllogism by proving

$$p \Rightarrow q; \qquad q \Rightarrow r.$$

6. Show that the result

$$(p \Rightarrow q) \Rightarrow (\sim q \Rightarrow \sim p)$$

contains its own converse by applying it to the statements $\sim q$ and $\sim p$.

7. Consider the following statements:
p = Both x and y are positive, unequal, real numbers;
$q = [x + y > 2\sqrt{xy}]$;
r = The arithmetic mean between x and y is greater than the geometric mean.
Illustrate the Law of the Syllogism by proving $p \Rightarrow q$, $q \Rightarrow r$.

8. In Exercises 5 and 7, give the contrapositive statements to

$$p \Rightarrow q; \qquad q \Rightarrow r; \qquad p \Rightarrow r.$$

9. In Exercises 5 and 7, which of the following statements have true converses?

(a) $p \Rightarrow q$, (b) $q \Rightarrow r$, (c) $p \Rightarrow r$,
(d) $q \Rightarrow p$, (e) $\sim p \Rightarrow \sim q$.

4.5. PRINCIPLES OF PROOF

So far we have spent much space on translation from English to squiggles, and vice versa. In this section, we wish to illustrate some of the types of classical mathematical proofs, that is, we shall discuss logic, not "logic".

If we know the answer to a problem which involves varying integral values of a parameter, then we can usually find a proof by the process of *Mathematical Induction.* Let us consider

Example 4.5.1. Prove that

$$\sum_{r=1}^{n} r^2 = \frac{n(n+1)(2n+1)}{6},$$

for all positive integral values of n.

The proof falls into three parts.

(a) Verify that the result is true for the first value of n. Clearly, for $n = 1$, the left-hand side is $1^2 = 1$, and the right-hand side is $1 \cdot 2 \cdot 3/6 = 1$. So the suggested formula is indeed true for $n = 1$.

(b) *Assume* that the result is true for a *specific* value k, that is,

$$1^2 + 2^2 + 3^2 + \cdots + k^2 = \frac{k(k+1)(2k+1)}{6}.$$

Add the $(k + 1)$th term of the series, namely, $(k + 1)^2$, to both sides. Then

$$\begin{aligned} 1^2 + 2^2 + \cdots + k^2 + (k+1)^2 \\ &= \frac{k(k+1)(2k+1)}{6} + (k+1)^2 \\ &= (k+1)\left[\frac{k(2k+1)}{6} + (k+1)\right] \\ &= \frac{(k+1)(2k^2+7k+6)}{6} \\ &= \frac{(k+1)(k+2)(2k+3)}{6} \\ &= \frac{(k+1)[(k+1)+1][2(k+1)+1]}{6}. \end{aligned}$$

But this result is exactly the result which would have been given by the suggested formula. Thus we have proved that *if* the given result holds for the sum of k terms, *then* it must also be true for the sum of $k + 1$ terms.

(c) From part (a), we know that the result is true for $n = 1$; and, from part (b), we know that whenever the result is true for any particular value, then it is true for the next integral value. So, we may argue: since the result holds for $n = 1$, it must hold for $n = 2$; since it holds for $n = 2$, then it must hold for $n = 3$; et cetera. By continuing this argument, we see that the result holds for any arbitrary integral value of n.

It is worth noting that part (c) is the same for almost all induction problems.

A second type of mathematical proof is afforded by the method of *Proof by Counterexample.* Many students, in giving a proof, verify a result for a particular case, and then think they have a general proof. They fail to realize that one, or even a hundred, examples of the truth of a result can never *prove* the result; but one single example of the falsehood of a result is quite sufficient to *disprove* the result.

Example 4.5.2. Show that $f(n) = n^2 + n + 41$ (n a non-negative integer) is not always a prime number.

The early values of $f(n)$ are 41, 43, 47, 53, 61, 71, 83, . . . , and they are all prime. Indeed, the first 40 values of $f(n)$ are all prime! However,

$$f(40) = 40^2 + 40 + 41 = 41^2,$$

which is not a prime. This single example suffices to prove that $f(n)$ is not always a prime number.

Finally, we mention a very potent method of proof, namely, the *Indirect Proof.* Very often a result can be established by showing that the converse result produces a contradiction, and so must be false. In other words, if p is a statement, then either p or $\sim p$ must be true. We then eliminate the possibility $\sim p$ by showing that $\sim p$ leads to a contradiction.

Example 4.5.3. Prove that $\sqrt{3}$ is not a rational number.

We start by assuming the statement

$$p = \text{The number } \sqrt{3} \text{ is a rational number } \frac{a}{b}\cdot$$

Here a and b are positive integers, and we take the fraction in its lowest terms, that is, a and b have no common factor greater than one. Then

$$3 = \frac{a^2}{b^2}, \qquad 3b^2 = a^2.$$

Since 3 is a factor of the left-hand side of this equation, it must divide the right-hand side. Thus, 3 is a factor of a; hence we may write $a = 3c$, and obtain

$$3b^2 = (3c)^2 = 9c^2; \qquad b^2 = 3c^2.$$

Since 3 is a factor of the right-hand side of this last equation, it must divide the left-hand side. Thus, 3 is a factor of b. But this shows that 3 is a factor of *both* a and b; this is false, since a and b had no common factor. Thus the assumption made originally, namely,

$$p = \text{The number } \sqrt{3} \text{ is a rational number } \frac{a}{b},$$

can not be true (since it led to a contradiction). We must then conclude that the converse statement,

$$\sim p = \text{The number } \sqrt{3} \text{ is not a rational number,}$$

must be true.

EXERCISES

1. Use mathematical induction to prove

$$\sum_{r=1}^{n} r^3 = \frac{n^2(n+1)^2}{4}.$$

2. Use mathematical induction to prove that

$$23^{3n} - 1$$

is divisible by 7 for all positive integers n.

3. By computing S_1, S_2, S_3, S_4, obtain a hypothetical formula for

$$S_n = \frac{1}{1 \cdot 2} + \frac{1}{2 \cdot 3} + \frac{1}{3 \cdot 4} + \cdots + \frac{1}{n(n+1)},$$

and prove your result by mathematical induction.

4. Prove that $\sqrt[3]{5}$ is not a rational number.

5. Prove that

$$x = 1 + \frac{1}{1!} + \frac{1}{2!} + \frac{1}{3!} + \frac{1}{4!} + \cdots$$

can not be rational. [*Hint:* Assume $x = m/n$; multiply both sides by $n!$, and thence derive a contradiction.]

6. Disprove the statement

$$f(n) = 2^{2^n} + 1 \text{ is a prime number for } n = 0, 1, 2, \ldots$$

by showing that 641 is a factor of $f(5)$.

4.6. BINARY NUMBERS AND COMPUTING

The dual nature of logical negation, typified by the tautology

$$p \cup (\sim p),$$

enters into the structure of modern electronic computers. Here we shall only remark that many electronic computers store numerical data on a magnetic drum. One can think of such a drum as bearing a huge number of tiny spots, each of which is magnetized in either one direction or the other. Consequently, we should be able to represent a number by spots on the drum, representing 0 by one direction of magnetization and 1 by the opposite direction, provided we were able to build a number up out of zeros and ones rather than out of the usual ten digits 0, 1, 2, 3, 4, 5, 6, 7, 8, 9. This is accomplished by using the binary scale of notation.

First, we recall the meaning of an ordinary number in the usual *scale of ten* (or the *decimal scale*); the integer 9327 means

$$9(10)^3 + 3(10)^2 + 2(10)^1 + 7(10)^0.$$

Similarly, 395.27 really means

$$3(10)^2 + 9(10)^1 + 5(10)^0 + 2(10)^{-1} + 7(10)^{-2}.$$

Other scales of notation are possible; thus, 356.3 (in the *scale of seven*) represents the number

$$3(7)^2 + 5(7)^1 + 6(7)^0 + 3(7)^{-1},$$

that is, $147 + 35 + 6 + \frac{3}{7} = 188\frac{3}{7}$ in the ordinary decimal scale.

In a similar fashion, 10111001 in the *scale of two* (or the *binary scale*) means

$$\begin{aligned}1(2)^7 + 0(2)^6 + 1(2)^5 + 1(2)^4 + 1(2)^3 + 0(2)^2 + 0(2)^1 + 1(2)^0 \\ = 128 + 32 + 16 + 8 + 1 = 185 \text{ (scale of 10)}.\end{aligned}$$

Consequently, we can convert any number into the binary scale by writing it in powers of 2. For instance,

$$\begin{aligned}5071 \text{ (scale of 10)} &= 4096 + 512 + 256 + 128 + 64 + 8 + 4 + 2 + 1 \\ &= 2^{12} + 2^9 + 2^8 + 2^7 + 2^6 + 2^3 + 2^2 + 2 + 1 \\ &= 1001111001111 \text{ (scale of 2)}.\end{aligned}$$

Decimals are handled in the same way; thus,

$$\begin{aligned}&1.3232\dot{3}\dot{2}\ldots \text{ (scale of 10)} \\ &\qquad = 1 + 3(10)^{-1} + 2(10)^{-2} + 3(10)^{-3} + 2(10)^{-4} + \cdots \\ &\qquad = 1 + \tfrac{30}{99} + \tfrac{2}{99} = \tfrac{132}{99}.\end{aligned}$$

On the other hand,

$$\begin{aligned}&111.0101\dot{0}\dot{1}\ldots \text{ (scale of 2)} \\ &\quad = 1(2)^2 + 1(2) + 1 + 0(2)^{-1} + 1(2)^{-2} + 0(2)^{-3} + 1(2)^{-4} + \cdots \\ &\quad = 4 + 2 + 1 + \frac{\frac{1}{4}}{1 - \frac{1}{4}} \\ &\quad = 7\tfrac{1}{3} \text{ (scale of 10)}.\end{aligned}$$

Computations within electronic computers are carried out in the binary scale (or in some coded variation thereof). For example,

```
    1101
    1011
    ----
    1101
   1101
  0000
 1101
--------
10001111
```

is the binary version of (13)(11) = 143 (scale of 10).

EXERCISES

1. Convert from the scale of 10 to the scale of 2:

   (a) 925.12, (b) 37.121212. . . .

2. Convert from the scale of 2 to the scale of 10:

   (a) 11010111.11111. . ., (b) 101.100100100. . .,

   (c) 111001.111011, (d) $10.\dot{1}110\dot{1}$.

3. Convert:

   (a) 927.5 from the scale of 10 to the scale of 5,

   (b) 431.020202. . . from the scale of 6 to the scale of 10.

4. Multiply 11011.1 by 1011110.01 in the scale of 2, and check your answer by converting the numbers to the scale of 10.

5. Perform the following problems in binary arithmetic, and check the results by conversion to the decimal scale:

   (a) (10110)(1101111), (b) $101\dot{0}10 + 1111111$,

   (c) 101111 + 110111, (d) 110110 − 1111,

   (e) $(101.011)^2$, (f) $(111.1)^2$,

   (g) 1/111, (h) 100 − 11.1,

   (i) 111011^3, (j) $1111^2 - 1101^2$.

5

Vector Spaces and Matrices

by Kenneth D. Fryer

5.1. VECTOR SPACES

We begin this section with two important definitions.

A *scalar* is an element from a fixed field. In the present discussion a scalar will simply be a real number (we refer the reader back to Chapter 1 for the properties of a field).

A *vector space* V is any collection of objects, precisely determined, satisfying rules (5.1.1)–(5.1.11).

(5.1.1) Corresponding to each pair of objects u and v in V, there is an object of V called the *sum* of u and v, written $u + v$ (in other words, V is closed under a binary operation called *addition*).

(5.1.2) Corresponding to each object u in V and each scalar (real number) λ, there is an object of V, called the *product* of λ and u, to be denoted λu (V is closed under an operation called *multiplication by a scalar*).

(5.1.3) One of the objects of V is to be singled out and called the *zero object*, denoted 0.

Finally, the objects in V and the system of scalars satisfy the following identities:

(5.1.4) $$u + v = v + u;$$

(5.1.5) $$u + (v + w) = (u + v) + w;$$

(5.1.6) $$\lambda(u + v) = \lambda u + \lambda v;$$

(5.1.7) $$(\lambda_1 + \lambda_2)u = \lambda_1 u + \lambda_2 u;$$

(5.1.8) $$\lambda_1(\lambda_2 u) = (\lambda_1 \lambda_2)u;$$

(5.1.9) $$1u = u;$$

(5.1.10) $$u + 0 = u;$$

(5.1.11) $$0u = 0.$$

The objects of the vector space V will be called *vectors*.

A vector space is, then, a collection of vectors which can be added together and which can be multiplied by scalars, the result in each case being again a vector; the identities (5.1.4)–(5.1.11) lay down the rules governing this addition and multiplication. Identities (5.1.4) and (5.1.5) state that addition of vectors is to be commutative and associative; (5.1.6) states that scalar multiplication is to be distributive over vector addition (this ensures, for example, that the vector $5(u + v)$ is the same as the vector $5u + 5v$); (5.1.7) states, for example, that the vector $2u + 3u$ is the same as the vector $5u$; (5.1.8) states that scalar multiplication is associative; for example, $2(3u)$ and $6u$ are the same vector; (5.1.9) states that the scalar unit 1 is also a unit under scalar multiplication; finally, (5.1.10) and (5.1.11) state that the zero vector behaves like the real number 0 under ordinary addition and multiplication.

The definition we have given for vector space is an axiomatic one; it describes a vector space but says nothing about the existence of such a mathematical system. We could define a *cowraffe* axiomatically as follows:

Definition. A *cowraffe* (Figure 5.1) is a cow satisfying the following condition:

It has a neck five feet long.

Such a definition describes completely a cowraffe but "no such animal exists". We ask then "Are there any mathematical systems which are indeed vector spaces?" This question is answered in the next section.

Figure 5.1

EXERCISES

1. Use the symbol $-u$ as an abbreviation for the vector $(-1)u$. Then verify that $u + (-u)$ is the zero vector.

2. Prove that for given vectors u, v, there is always a vector x such that $u + x = v$.

3. By $u - v$ we shall mean $u + (-v)$; verify:

   (i) $\lambda(u - v) = \lambda u - \lambda v$; (ii) $u + v - w = u - w + v$.

5.2. THE CARTESIAN SPACE OF DIMENSION 2

Consider the collection of all ordered pairs (a, b) of real numbers. We speak of a and b as the components of the number pair. We wish to show that this collection gives an example of a vector space. These pairs of numbers are not numbers (which we know how to add and multiply), but are mathematical objects, and hence we must specify how they are to be added, and how multiplied by scalars. We define addition in (5.2.1), scalar multiplication in (5.2.2), and select a zero vector in (5.2.3) below.

(5.2.1) $$(a_1, a_2) + (b_1, b_2) = (a_1 + b_1, a_2 + b_2);$$

(5.2.2) $$\lambda(a_1, a_2) = (\lambda a_1, \lambda a_2) \qquad \text{for any real number } \lambda;$$

(5.2.3) $$0 = (0, 0).$$

Thus, to add two pairs, we simply add their corresponding components; to multiply a number pair by a scalar, we multiply each component by that scalar. For example,

$$(2, 3) + (3, -2) = (5, 1);$$

$$(2, 3) + (-2, -3) = (0, 0);$$

$$10(2, 3) = (20, 30).$$

Note that our definition had to be, and is, such that the sum of two number pairs and the scalar multiple of a number pair is again a number pair. The selection of the number pair (0, 0) as the zero object is a logical one since, using definition (5.2.1) for addition, $(a, b) + (0, 0) = (a, b)$, as required in identity (5.1.10).

Finally, *we define two number pairs to be equal if and only if their corresponding components are equal*, that is, $(a, b) = (c, d)$ if and only if $a = c$ and $b = d$. We are now in a position to prove

THEOREM 5.2.1. *The collection of all pairs* (a, b) *of real numbers is a vector space under the definitions (5.2.1), (5.2.2), (5.2.3).*

Proof. We need only verify that identities (5.1.4)–(5.1.11) hold. We will verify (5.1.6), and leave the verification of the remainder to the reader.

Verification of (5.1.6). Let $u = (a_1, a_2)$, $v = (b_1, b_2)$; then

$$\begin{aligned} \lambda(u + v) &= \lambda[(a_1, a_2) + (b_1, b_2)] \\ &= \lambda(a_1 + b_1, a_2 + b_2), && \text{from (5.2.1)}, \\ &= [\lambda(a_1 + b_1), \lambda(a_2 + b_2)], && \text{from (5.2.2)}, \\ &= (\lambda a_1 + \lambda b_1, \lambda a_2 + \lambda b_2), \end{aligned}$$

since multiplication of real numbers is distributive over addition,

$$\begin{aligned} &= (\lambda a_1, \lambda a_2) + (\lambda b_1, \lambda b_2), && \text{from (5.2.1)}, \\ &= \lambda(a_1, a_2) + \lambda(b_1, b_2), && \text{from (5.2.2)}, \\ &= \lambda u + \lambda v, && \text{as required.} \end{aligned}$$

As examples of the application of these identities, we have

(a) $5(2, 3) + 2(-1, 5) = (10, 15) + (-2, 10) = (8, 25)$,

(b) $4(-1, 3) + 2(2, -6) = (-4, 12) + (4, -12) = (0, 0)$.

The vectors (a, b) are also called *row vectors* of *length* 2, and the vector space they form is also called a *Cartesian space* of *dimension* 2.

The Cartesian space of dimension 3 will be the vector space of all triples (a, b, c) of real numbers under definitions of addition and scalar multiplication similar to those in (5.2.1) and (5.2.2); $(0, 0, 0)$ will be the zero vector. Indeed, we may generalize to the Cartesian space of dimension n consisting of all n-tuples $(a_1, a_2, \ldots, a_n)$ of real numbers.

It is sometimes more convenient to consider column vectors

$$\begin{pmatrix} a_1 \\ a_2 \end{pmatrix}, \quad \begin{pmatrix} a_1 \\ a_2 \\ a_3 \end{pmatrix}, \quad \ldots, \quad \begin{pmatrix} a_1 \\ a_2 \\ \cdot \\ \cdot \\ \cdot \\ a_n \end{pmatrix}.$$

This again leads us to Cartesian spaces of dimensions $2, 3, \ldots, n$. Indeed, there is an obvious one-to-one correspondence between the elements of the Cartesian space of row vectors (a_1, a_2) and the Cartesian space of column vectors $\begin{pmatrix} a_1 \\ a_2 \end{pmatrix}$ (and, similarly, for the spaces of higher dimension). These spaces are isomorphic, that is, the corresponding elements in each space behave in exactly the same manner; only their appearance is different.

There is an obvious one-to-one correspondence between the vectors (x, y) of the Cartesian space of dimension 2 and the points (x, y) of the Euclidean plane. We can think of the point (x, y) in the Euclidean plane as being the end point of the physical vector with initial point at the origin. In this way we can identify the vectors of the Cartesian space of dimension 2 over the real numbers with the physical vectors in the Cartesian plane (each vector in the Cartesian plane is equal to some vector with its initial point at the origin). A similar identification can be made of the vectors of the Cartesian space of dimension 3 over the real numbers (the collection of all triples (x, y, z) of real numbers) with the physical vectors in 3-space having the origin as their initial point.

It can then be seen that addition and scalar multiplication of vectors in a vector space correspond exactly to addition (using the parallelogram law) and scalar multiplication of physical vectors in 2 and 3 dimensions. Note that we do not need this physical interpretation of vector spaces in order to talk about vectors (it is obviously a nice thing to have whenever possible).

Thus we may speak of vectors in 4 dimensions, 5 dimensions, n dimensions, or an infinite number of dimensions, even though a physical space with these dimensions may not be realizable.

These ideas are amplified in Section 5.5. In this section vectors are used to introduce elementary trigonometry and develop some of the formulae of trigonometry and geometry.

EXERCISES

1. Verify that identities (5.1.4)–(5.1.11) hold for the collection of n-tuples $(a_1, a_2, \ldots, a_n)$ of real numbers under suitable definitions of addition and scalar multiplication of n-tuples.
2. Let $u = (2, 1, 2, 0, -1)$, $v = (3, 1, 2, -1, 0)$, $w = (-3, -2, 1, 8, 1)$; find (a) $2u + 3v - 4w$; (b) $-3u + v + 2w$.
3. Let $u = (2, 1, -2), v = (-4, 2, 3), w = (-8, 8, 5), x = (1, 3, 5)$. Show that there is a real number λ for which $2u + \lambda v = w$, but that there are no real numbers λ and μ for which $\lambda u + \mu v = x$.

5.3. THE VECTOR SPACE OF 2 × 2 MATRICES

Consider all square arrays of two rows and two columns of real numbers (in general the elements can be from any fixed field):

$$A = \begin{pmatrix} a_{11} & a_{12} \\ a_{21} & a_{22} \end{pmatrix}$$

(the entry a_{ij} indicates the number in the ith row and jth column). Such an array is called a *matrix* of *dimension* 2×2. The numbers a_{ij} are the *components* of the matrix. Two 2×2 matrices are *equal* if and only if their corresponding components are equal. Let

$$B = \begin{pmatrix} b_{11} & b_{12} \\ b_{21} & b_{22} \end{pmatrix}$$

be a second 2×2 matrix. Again, these arrays of numbers are not numbers but mathematical objects; so we define addition of 2×2 matrices, multiplication of such a matrix by a scalar, and the zero matrix in (5.3.1), (5.3.2), and (5.3.3) below.

$$(5.3.1) \qquad A + B = \begin{pmatrix} a_{11} + b_{11} & a_{12} + b_{12} \\ a_{21} + b_{21} & a_{22} + b_{22} \end{pmatrix};$$

$$(5.3.2) \qquad \lambda A = \begin{pmatrix} \lambda a_{11} & \lambda a_{12} \\ \lambda a_{21} & \lambda a_{22} \end{pmatrix}, \qquad \text{for any real number } \lambda;$$

$$(5.3.3) \qquad 0 = \begin{pmatrix} 0 & 0 \\ 0 & 0 \end{pmatrix} \qquad \text{(the zero matrix).}$$

THEOREM 5.3.1. *The collection of all such 2×2 matrices is a vector space under the definitions (5.3.1), (5.3.2), (5.3.3).*

Proof. We need merely verify that identities (5.1.4)–(5.1.11) hold for these matrices. We will verify (5.1.5), and leave the verification of the remaining identities as an exercise for the reader.

Verification of (5.1.5). $A + (B + C) = (A + B) + C.$

$$A + (B + C) = \begin{pmatrix} a_{11} & a_{12} \\ a_{21} & a_{22} \end{pmatrix} + \left[\begin{pmatrix} b_{11} & b_{12} \\ b_{21} & b_{22} \end{pmatrix} + \begin{pmatrix} c_{11} & c_{12} \\ c_{21} & c_{22} \end{pmatrix}\right]$$

$$= \begin{pmatrix} a_{11} & a_{12} \\ a_{21} & a_{22} \end{pmatrix} + \begin{pmatrix} b_{11} + c_{11} & b_{12} + c_{12} \\ b_{21} + c_{21} & b_{22} + c_{22} \end{pmatrix} \qquad \text{using (5.3.1)}$$

$$= \begin{pmatrix} a_{11} + (b_{11} + c_{11}) & a_{12} + (b_{12} + c_{12}) \\ a_{21} + (b_{21} + c_{21}) & a_{22} + (b_{22} + c_{22}) \end{pmatrix} \qquad \text{using (5.3.1)}$$

$$= \begin{pmatrix} (a_{11} + b_{11}) + c_{11} & (a_{12} + b_{12}) + c_{12} \\ (a_{21} + b_{21}) + c_{21} & (a_{22} + b_{22}) + c_{22} \end{pmatrix}$$

(since addition of real numbers is associative—see Chapter 1)

$$= \begin{pmatrix} a_{11} + b_{11} & a_{12} + b_{12} \\ a_{21} + b_{21} & a_{22} + b_{22} \end{pmatrix} + \begin{pmatrix} c_{11} & c_{12} \\ c_{21} & c_{22} \end{pmatrix} \qquad \text{using (5.3.1)}$$

$$= \left[\begin{pmatrix} a_{11} & a_{12} \\ a_{21} & a_{22} \end{pmatrix} + \begin{pmatrix} b_{11} & b_{12} \\ b_{21} & b_{22} \end{pmatrix}\right] + \begin{pmatrix} c_{11} & c_{12} \\ c_{21} & c_{22} \end{pmatrix} \qquad \text{using (5.3.1)}$$

$$= (A + B) + C.$$

The vector space of 2×2 matrices can be generalized to the vector space of all $m \times n$ matrices (an $m \times n$ matrix is a rectangular array of m rows and n columns of scalars from a fixed field) with addition of $m \times n$ matrices, multiplication of an $m \times n$ matrix by a scalar, and the existence of a zero $m \times n$ matrix as in definitions similar to (5.3.1), (5.3.2), and (5.3.3).

EXERCISES

1. Verify identities (5.1.4)–(5.1.11) for the collection of all 2×3 matrices.

2. Let $A = \begin{pmatrix} 3 & 2 & -1 \\ 1 & 3 & 0 \end{pmatrix}$, $B = \begin{pmatrix} -1 & 2 & 4 \\ 2 & 1 & 1 \end{pmatrix}$; find

   (a) $A + B$,
   (b) $A - B$ [defined as $A + (-1)B$],
   (c) $2A + 3B$,
   (d) a matrix C such that $A - 3B + C = 0$.

3. Let $A = \begin{pmatrix} 2 & 3 & 4 \\ -1 & 0 & 2 \end{pmatrix}$, $B = \begin{pmatrix} 3 & 1 & 2 \\ -2 & 0 & 1 \end{pmatrix}$, $C = \begin{pmatrix} 4 & 2 & 3 \\ 7 & 4 & -3 \end{pmatrix}$; find

(a) $A + 2B - 3C$, (b) $-3A + B + 2C$,

(c) D so that $A + 2D = 3B$.

5.4. MULTIPLICATION OF MATRICES

The definition of vector space does not require an operation of "multiplication" (indeed if a vector space possesses a multiplication for vectors which obeys the laws of closure, associativity, and distributivity over addition, it is then a mathematical system which is called an *algebra*). In the present section we proceed to define a multiplication for matrices. We intimated in Section 5.3 that addition is defined only for matrices having the same dimension; the definition subsequently given for matrix addition (the adding of corresponding components) then appeared to be a logical one. Multiplication of matrices also involves a restriction on the dimensions of the matrices involved, as we shall see below. The definition given for matrix multiplication is *not* superficially a logical one (we do not simply multiply corresponding components), and we shall illustrate its derivation for 2×2 matrices by a consideration of linear transformations involving two variables (the method is perfectly general and may be used to derive the multiplication rule for all matrices).

The equations

(5.4.1) $$T_1 \begin{cases} x' = 2x + 3y, \\ y' = x - y, \end{cases}$$

produce a *mapping* or *transformation* T_1 of the Euclidean plane onto itself; the result of performing the operation T_1 will carry a point (x, y) into a point (x', y') [this will be expressed as $T_1(x, y) = (x', y')$]. Thus the point $(1, 1)$ is carried into (or made to correspond with) the point $(5, 0)$, that is, $T_1(1, 1) = (5, 0)$, read as: "when transformation T_1 operates on point $(1, 1)$, it produces the point $(5, 0)$", or "point $(5, 0)$ is the *image* of point $(1, 1)$ under the mapping T_1". Again, $T_1(2, 3) = (13, -1)$, etc. Solving (5.4.1) for x and y in terms of x' and y' yields

(5.4.2) $$T_1^* \begin{cases} x = \frac{1}{5}x' + \frac{3}{5}y', \\ y = \frac{1}{5}x' - \frac{2}{5}y'. \end{cases}$$

This transformation (call it T_1^*) is the inverse of T_1; it carries the point $(5, 0)$ back into $(1, 1)$, that is, $T_1^*(5, 0) = (1, 1)$. Again, $T_1^*(13, -1) = (2, 3)$, etc.

Note that the transformation is determined not by the letters or variables (or placeholders!) involved (the x, y, x', y'), but by their coefficients, which, as they stand, form a rectangular array, that is, a 2×2 matrix. Thus the transformation T_1 in (5.4.1) is represented by (or *is*) the matrix

$$A = \begin{pmatrix} 2 & 3 \\ 1 & -1 \end{pmatrix},$$

and that in (5.4.2) by the matrix

$$A^* = \begin{pmatrix} \frac{1}{5} & \frac{3}{5} \\ \frac{1}{5} & -\frac{2}{5} \end{pmatrix}.$$

Suppose now that we have a second mapping

$$\text{(5.4.3)} \qquad T_2 \begin{cases} x'' = x' + y', \\ y'' = 3x' - y', \end{cases}$$

which carries points (x', y') into points (x'', y''), that is,

$$T_2(x', y') = (x'', y'');$$

T_2 is thus represented by the matrix

$$B = \begin{pmatrix} 1 & 1 \\ 3 & -1 \end{pmatrix}.$$

If we first carry out mapping T_1 on (x, y) to produce (x', y'), and then carry out T_2 on (x', y'), we produce a mapping of points (x, y) onto points (x'', y''). We call this mapping the *product* of the transformations T_1 and T_2, and write it as $T_2 \,\theta\, T_1$; thus

$$T_2 \,\theta\, T_1(x, y) = (x'', y'').$$

Algebraically, we have

$$\text{(5.4.4)} \quad T_2 \,\theta\, T_1 \begin{cases} x'' = x' + y' = (2x + 3y) + (x - y) = 3x + 2y, \\ y'' = 3x' - y' = (6x + 9y) - (x - y) = 5x + 10y; \end{cases}$$

so that the transformation resulting from the product $T_2 \,\theta\, T_1$ of the two mappings is determined by the matrix

$$C = \begin{pmatrix} 3 & 2 \\ 5 & 10 \end{pmatrix}.$$

We would like this matrix to be the "product" $B \,\theta\, A$ (or simply BA) of the two matrices B and A which determine T_2 and T_1.

If we use general expressions for the mappings T_1 and T_2, namely,

$$\text{(5.4.5)} \qquad T_1 \begin{cases} x' = a_{11}x + a_{12}y, \\ y' = a_{21}x + a_{22}y, \end{cases} \qquad T_2 \begin{cases} x'' = b_{11}x' + b_{12}y', \\ y'' = b_{21}x' + b_{22}y', \end{cases}$$

we obtain

$$(5.4.6) \qquad T_2 \theta T_1 \begin{cases} x'' = (a_{11}b_{11} + a_{21}b_{12})x + (a_{12}b_{11} + a_{22}b_{12})y, \\ y'' = (a_{11}b_{21} + a_{21}b_{22})x + (a_{12}b_{21} + a_{22}b_{22})y; \end{cases}$$

so we *define* multiplication of second-order (2×2) matrices to be

$$\begin{pmatrix} b_{11} & b_{12} \\ b_{21} & b_{22} \end{pmatrix} \begin{pmatrix} a_{11} & a_{12} \\ a_{21} & a_{22} \end{pmatrix} = \begin{pmatrix} a_{11}b_{11} + a_{21}b_{12} & a_{12}b_{11} + a_{22}b_{12} \\ a_{11}b_{21} + a_{21}b_{22} & a_{12}b_{21} + a_{22}b_{22} \end{pmatrix}.$$

Note that the element in the *first row* and *first column* of the product matrix is the sum of products of elements in the *first row* of B multiplied by the corresponding elements in the *first column* of A; the element in the *first row* and *second column* of BA is the sum of the products of elements in the *first row* of B times the corresponding elements in the *second column* of A. In general, the element in the ith *row* and jth *column* of BA is the sum of the products of the elements in the ith *row* of B times the corresponding elements of the jth *column* of A. This is, in fact, the way in which multiplication of matrices in general is defined, whenever such multiplication is possible (note that, in order for this definition to have meaning, the columns of A must contain the same number of elements as the rows of B; thus, if B is an $m \times n$ matrix, A must be an $n \times r$ matrix in order that the product BA can be defined).

Using this definition of multiplication for the matrices

$$A = \begin{pmatrix} 2 & 3 \\ 1 & -1 \end{pmatrix}, \qquad B = \begin{pmatrix} 1 & 1 \\ 3 & -1 \end{pmatrix},$$

corresponding to the transformations T_1 of (5.4.1) and T_2 of (5.4.3), we have

$$BA = \begin{pmatrix} 1 & 1 \\ 3 & -1 \end{pmatrix} \begin{pmatrix} 2 & 3 \\ 1 & -1 \end{pmatrix} = \begin{pmatrix} 1(2) + 1(1) & 1(3) + 1(-1) \\ 3(2) + (-1)(1) & 3(3) + (-1)(-1) \end{pmatrix}$$

$$= \begin{pmatrix} 3 & 2 \\ 5 & 10 \end{pmatrix},$$

whereas

$$AB = \begin{pmatrix} 2 & 3 \\ 1 & -1 \end{pmatrix} \begin{pmatrix} 1 & 1 \\ 3 & -1 \end{pmatrix} = \begin{pmatrix} 2(1) + 3(3) & 2(1) + 3(-1) \\ 1(1) + (-1)3 & 1(1) + (-1)(-1) \end{pmatrix}$$

$$= \begin{pmatrix} 11 & -1 \\ -2 & 2 \end{pmatrix};$$

thus multiplication of matrices is not always commutative. Again, for matrices

$$A = \begin{pmatrix} 2 & 3 \\ 1 & -1 \end{pmatrix}, \qquad A^* = \begin{pmatrix} \frac{1}{5} & \frac{3}{5} \\ \frac{1}{5} & -\frac{2}{5} \end{pmatrix},$$

corresponding to transformations T_1 of (5.4.1) and T_1^* of (5.4.2), we have

$$AA^* = \begin{pmatrix} 2 & 3 \\ 1 & -1 \end{pmatrix}\begin{pmatrix} \frac{1}{5} & \frac{3}{5} \\ \frac{1}{5} & -\frac{2}{5} \end{pmatrix} = \begin{pmatrix} 1 & 0 \\ 0 & 1 \end{pmatrix}.$$

The matrix

$$I = \begin{pmatrix} 1 & 0 \\ 0 & 1 \end{pmatrix}$$

is an *identity* or *unit matrix* under the multiplication of 2×2 matrices; for every 2×2 matrix A we have $IA = AI = A$ (this is left for the reader to verify). The matrix A^* above is said to be the *inverse* of matrix A and is usually denoted by A^{-1}. We define A^2 to equal AA and, for m a positive integer, A^m is equal to the product $(A^{m-1})A$. We define A^{-m} to be $(A^{-1})^m$ and finally, $A^0 = I$. With these definitions, it is easy to see that the ordinary index laws hold for integral powers of matrices.

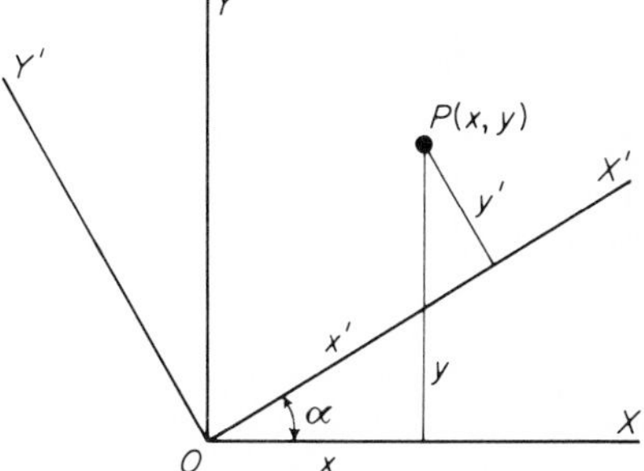

Figure 5.2

Consider a final example from geometry. Let the axes OX and OY be rotated about O through an angle α to the positions OX' and OY' (Figure 5.2). The equations giving the coordinates (x, y) of any point referred to OX and OY in terms of its coordinates (x', y') referred to OX' and OY' are called the equations for rotating the axes; these are

$$(5.4.7) \qquad \begin{cases} x = x' \cos \alpha - y' \sin \alpha, \\ y = x' \sin \alpha + y' \cos \alpha. \end{cases}$$

The matrix determining this transformation is

$$P_\alpha = \begin{pmatrix} \cos \alpha & -\sin \alpha \\ \sin \alpha & \cos \alpha \end{pmatrix}.$$

The matrix determining a rotation of axes through angle β is then

$$P_\beta = \begin{pmatrix} \cos \beta & -\sin \beta \\ \sin \beta & \cos \beta \end{pmatrix};$$

so

$$P_\beta P_\alpha = \begin{pmatrix} \cos\beta & -\sin\beta \\ \sin\beta & \cos\beta \end{pmatrix} \begin{pmatrix} \cos\alpha & -\sin\alpha \\ \sin\alpha & \cos\alpha \end{pmatrix}$$

$$= \begin{pmatrix} \cos\beta\cos\alpha - \sin\beta\sin\alpha & -\cos\beta\sin\alpha - \sin\beta\cos\alpha \\ \sin\beta\cos\alpha + \cos\beta\sin\alpha & -\sin\beta\sin\alpha + \cos\beta\cos\alpha \end{pmatrix}$$

$$= \begin{pmatrix} \cos(\beta+\alpha) & -\sin(\beta+\alpha) \\ \sin(\beta+\alpha) & \cos(\beta+\alpha) \end{pmatrix} = P_{\beta+\alpha}.$$

This is the matrix of the "product" of the transformations—the mapping obtained by first rotating axes through angle α and then through angle β, and is the mapping determined by rotating axes through angle $\alpha + \beta$.

If we solve equations (5.4.7) for x' and y' in terms of x and y, we obtain

(5.4.8)
$$\begin{cases} x' = x\cos\alpha + y\sin\alpha, \\ y' = -x\sin\alpha + y\cos\alpha. \end{cases}$$

This transformation is the inverse of the transformation in (5.4.7), and the matrix

$$\begin{pmatrix} \cos\alpha & \sin\alpha \\ -\sin\alpha & \cos\alpha \end{pmatrix}$$

is the inverse of matrix P_α, since

$$(P_\alpha)^{-1}P_\alpha = \begin{pmatrix} \cos\alpha & \sin\alpha \\ -\sin\alpha & \cos\alpha \end{pmatrix} \begin{pmatrix} \cos\alpha & -\sin\alpha \\ \sin\alpha & \cos\alpha \end{pmatrix}$$

$$= \begin{pmatrix} \cos^2\alpha + \sin^2\alpha & 0 \\ 0 & \sin^2\alpha + \cos^2\alpha \end{pmatrix}$$

$$= \begin{pmatrix} 1 & 0 \\ 0 & 1 \end{pmatrix}.$$

Note that we can write

$$P_\alpha^{-1} = \begin{pmatrix} \cos(-\alpha) & -\sin(-\alpha) \\ \sin(-\alpha) & \cos(-\alpha) \end{pmatrix} = P_{-\alpha}.$$

Thus the inverse of the operation P_α, which represents a rotation through angle α, is an operation $P_{-\alpha}$ which represents a rotation through angle $(-\alpha)$; the combination of the two matrices produces the identity matrix P_0,

$$P_\alpha P_{-\alpha} = P_0;$$

that is, P_0 represents the rotation through an angle zero, or simply the transformation $x'' = x, y'' = y$.

EXERCISES

1. Show that $P_\alpha P_\beta = P_\beta P_\alpha$ for the matrices above. Why is this?

2. Find the inverse of the matrix

$$\begin{pmatrix} 3 & 2 \\ -1 & 4 \end{pmatrix}.$$

[*Hint:* Write the transformation having this matrix and giving x', y', in terms of x, y; solve for x, y, in terms of x', y'.]

3. Given

$$A = \begin{pmatrix} 1 & 3 & 1 \\ 2 & 2 & 3 \\ -1 & 0 & 2 \end{pmatrix}, \qquad B = \begin{pmatrix} 2 & 4 & -1 \\ 1 & 3 & -2 \\ 0 & 1 & 4 \end{pmatrix},$$

find AB, BA, A^2, B^2, A^2B^2, and $(AB)^2$.

4. Given

$$A = \begin{pmatrix} 2 & 0 & 3 \\ 1 & 2 & 2 \\ -1 & 4 & 2 \end{pmatrix}, \qquad B = \begin{pmatrix} 1 \\ 2 \\ 6 \end{pmatrix},$$

find AB.

5. Given

$$A = \begin{pmatrix} 3 & 2 & 4 \\ 1 & 1 & 2 \\ -1 & 0 & 5 \end{pmatrix}, \quad X = \begin{pmatrix} x_1 \\ x_2 \\ x_3 \end{pmatrix}, \quad B = \begin{pmatrix} 2 \\ 1 \\ 4 \end{pmatrix},$$

show that the equations

$$\begin{aligned} 3x_1 + 2x_2 + 4x_3 &= 2 \\ x_1 + x_2 + 2x_3 &= 1 \\ -x_1 \qquad\quad + 5x_3 &= 4 \end{aligned}$$

can be written as the matrix equation $AX = B$.

6. (a) Write the equation

$$\begin{aligned} 2x_1 - x_2 &= 1 \\ x_1 + 2x_2 &= 5 \end{aligned}$$

as a single matrix equation $AX = B$.

(b) Find the inverse matrix A^{-1} of A.

(c) Multiply both sides of equation $AX = B$ by A^{-1} to obtain

$$\begin{aligned} A^{-1}(AX) &= A^{-1}B; \\ IX &= A^{-1}B; \\ X &= A^{-1}B. \end{aligned}$$

Identify components of the matrices X and $A^{-1}B$, thus solving the given system of equations for x_1, x_2.

5.5. VECTOR TRIGONOMETRY

In Section 5.1 we identified the vector (x, y) of the Cartesian space of dimension 2 over the real numbers with the point (x, y) in the Cartesian plane, and, indeed, with the directed line segment with initial point at the origin and terminal point at (x, y). Each such line segment is the representative of an infinite number of line segments with equal lengths and identical directions (directions measured counterclockwise from the positive x-axis).

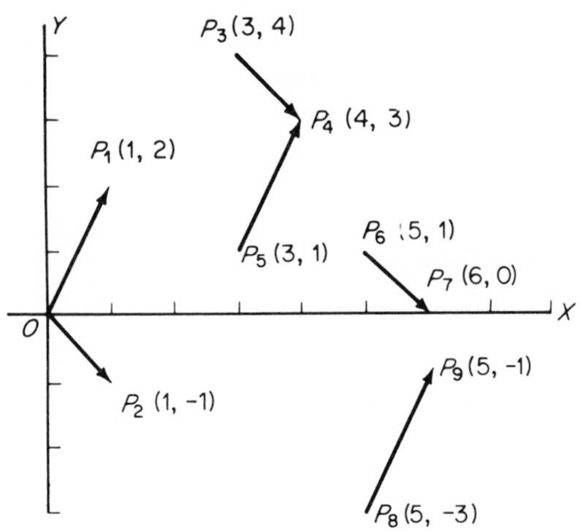

Figure 5.3

Figure 5.3 illustrates the fact; $\overrightarrow{OP_1}$ (the arrow indicates that the line segment is directed from O to P_1) has the same length and direction as $\overrightarrow{P_5P_4}$ and $\overrightarrow{P_8P_9}$, and $\overrightarrow{OP_2}$ has the same length and direction as $\overrightarrow{P_3P_4}$ and $\overrightarrow{P_6P_7}$.

Thus the pair (a, b) of real numbers determines an infinite number of line segments of equal lengths and directions; we say that the vector (a, b) *is* this entire collection of directed line segments. We define the *length* of the vector $\mathbf{v} = (a, b)$ to be $|\mathbf{v}| = \sqrt{a^2 + b^2}$; a vector with length 1 is called a *unit vector*. Thus, the vector $(4, -3)$ has length 5, and the vector $(-2/\sqrt{5}, 1/\sqrt{5})$ is a unit vector.

We have already defined equality of vectors (Section 5.1); an application of similar triangles will show that the vectors (a, b) and $\lambda(a, b) = (\lambda a, \lambda b)$ have the same direction. Thus, for a given direction (specified by the angle θ measured counterclockwise from the positive x-axis), there is an infinite number of vectors $(\lambda a, \lambda b)$, with $\lambda < 0$, having the same direction and differing only in length. These vectors have another feature in common, namely, the pair of real numbers formed by dividing each component of the vector by the length of the vector; thus the vectors $(\lambda a, \lambda b)$ determine the number pair

$$\frac{\lambda a}{\sqrt{(\lambda a)^2 + (\lambda b)^2}} = \frac{a}{\sqrt{a^2 + b^2}},$$

$$\frac{\lambda b}{\sqrt{(\lambda a)^2 + (\lambda b)^2}} = \frac{b}{\sqrt{a^2 + b^2}},$$

for all values of $\lambda < 0$.

For the vector $\mathbf{v} = (a, b)$, we notice that one of the directed line segments determined by the vector $\mathbf{v}$ is that line segment from the origin $(0, 0)$ to the point (a, b); if θ is the direction of this line segment, and hence the direction of all line segments determined by $\mathbf{v}$, it is clear from Figure 5.4 that

$$\cos\theta = \frac{a}{\sqrt{a^2 + b^2}},$$

$$\sin\theta = \frac{b}{\sqrt{a^2 + b^2}}.$$

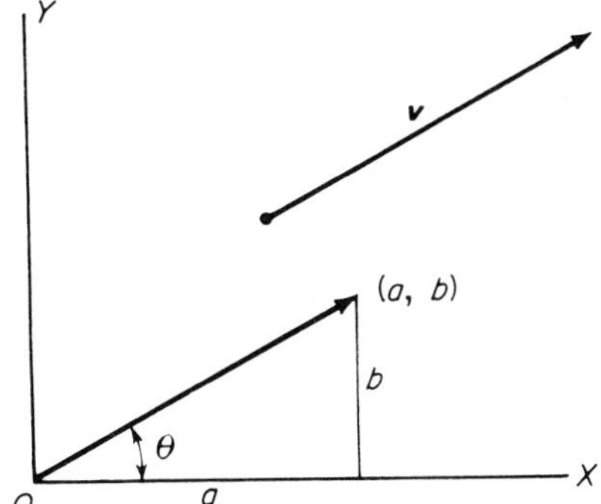

Figure 5.4

We now define the *direction cosines* of the vector $\mathbf{v}$ to be these two numbers $\cos\theta$ and $\sin\theta$. The following observations are immediate:

(a) vectors with the same direction have the same direction cosines, that is, direction cosines depend only on the direction of the vector and not on its length;

(b) $-1 \leq \cos\theta \leq 1$, $-1 \leq \sin\theta \leq 1$;

(c) $\cos^2\theta + \sin^2\theta = 1$.

Now consider those representatives of unit vectors $\boldsymbol{\epsilon}_\theta$ which have their initial point at the origin of a Cartesian coordinate system, and which make an angle θ with the positive x-axis; their terminal points will lie on the unit circle with centre at the origin. Then the coordinates of the terminal point of the representative $\boldsymbol{\epsilon}_\theta$ will obviously be $(\cos\theta, \sin\theta)$; cf. Figure 5.5.

Since $\boldsymbol{\epsilon}_0 = (\cos 0, \sin 0) = (1, 0)$, we have $\cos 0 = 1$ and $\sin 0 = 0$; since

$$\boldsymbol{\epsilon}_{\pi/2} = \left(\cos\frac{\pi}{2}, \sin\frac{\pi}{2}\right) = (0, 1),$$

we have $\cos\pi/2 = 0$ and $\sin\pi/2 = 1$. Similarly, the sines and cosines of the usual familiar angles may be obtained.

Again, a consideration of ϵ_θ and $\epsilon_{(-\theta)}$ in Figure 5.5, together with an application of congruent triangles, shows that

$$\cos(-\theta) = \cos\theta \quad \text{and} \quad \sin(-\theta) = -\sin\theta.$$

Other results may be obtained in this way; for example, $\cos(\pi/2 - \theta) = \sin\theta$, etc.

A very important result is the formula

$$\cos(\alpha - \beta) = \cos\alpha\cos\beta + \sin\alpha\sin\beta. \tag{5.5.1}$$

To establish this result, consider vectors ϵ_α and ϵ_β (Figure 5.6); relative to the x-y coordinates axes, the end points P_1 and P_2 of these vectors will

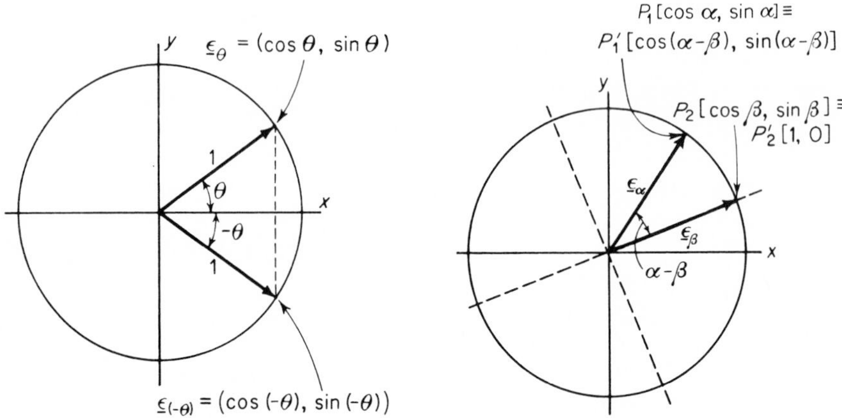

Figure 5.5

Figure 5.6

have coordinates $(\cos\alpha, \sin\alpha)$ and $(\cos\beta, \sin\beta)$, respectively; with respect to an x'-y' coordinate system (where the x'-axis is taken along vector ϵ_β), these points have coordinates $[\cos(\alpha - \beta), \sin(\alpha - \beta)]$ and $[1, 0]$ respectively. The distance $\overline{P_1P_2}$ is independent of the coordinate system, and we have

$$\begin{aligned}\overline{P_1P_2}^2 &= (\cos\alpha - \cos\beta)^2 + (\sin\alpha - \sin\beta)^2 \\ &= 2 - 2(\cos\alpha\cos\beta + \sin\alpha\sin\beta);\end{aligned}$$

also

$$\begin{aligned}\overline{P_1P_2}^2 &= [\cos(\alpha - \beta) - 1]^2 + \sin^2(\alpha - \beta) \\ &= 2 - 2\cos(\alpha - \beta).\end{aligned}$$

Relation (5.5.1) follows immediately, and it is then easy to verify algebraically that

$$\sin(\alpha - \beta) = \sin\alpha\cos\beta - \cos\alpha\sin\beta. \tag{5.5.2}$$

The results in (5.5.1) and (5.5.2) may be generalized in

THEOREM 5.5.1. Let $\mathbf{u} = (a_1, b_1)$ and $\mathbf{v} = (a_2, b_2)$ be vectors such that the counterclockwise angle from $\mathbf{u}$ to $\mathbf{v}$ is θ; then

$$\cos \theta = \frac{a_1 a_2 + b_1 b_2}{\sqrt{a_1^2 + b_1^2}\sqrt{a_2^2 + b_2^2}},$$

that is, $|\mathbf{u}|\,|\mathbf{v}| \cos \theta = a_1 a_2 + b_1 b_2$; and

$$\sin \theta = \frac{a_1 b_2 - a_2 b_1}{\sqrt{a_1^2 + b_1^2}\sqrt{a_2^2 + b_2^2}},$$

that is, $|\mathbf{u}|\,|\mathbf{v}| \sin \theta = a_1 b_2 - a_2 b_1$.

The results of Theorem 5.5.1 follow immediately from (5.5.1) and (5.5.2); for $\mathbf{u}$ has direction cosines

$$\frac{a_1}{\sqrt{a_1^2 + b_1^2}}, \qquad \frac{b_1}{\sqrt{a_1^2 + b_1^2}},$$

and $\mathbf{v}$ has direction cosines

$$\frac{a_2}{\sqrt{a_2^2 + b_2^2}}, \qquad \frac{b_2}{\sqrt{a_2^2 + b_2^2}}.$$

θ is then just the angle $\alpha - \beta$ where α and β specify the direction angles of $\mathbf{u}$ and $\mathbf{v}$ respectively.

Now let us make certain definitions. For vectors $\mathbf{u} = (a_1, b_1)$ and $\mathbf{v} = (a_2, b_2)$, with contained angle θ, we define the *scalar product* $\mathbf{u} \cdot \mathbf{v}$ of $\mathbf{u}$ and $\mathbf{v}$ to be $a_1 a_2 + b_1 b_2$, and we define a new vector $\mathbf{u} \times \mathbf{v}$, called the *vector product* of $\mathbf{u}$ and $\mathbf{v}$, to be a vector perpendicular to the plane of $\mathbf{u}$ and $\mathbf{v}$ and with magnitude $a_1 b_2 - a_2 b_1$; thus

(5.5.3) $$\mathbf{u} \cdot \mathbf{v} = a_1 a_2 + b_1 b_2 = |\mathbf{u}|\,|\mathbf{v}| \cos \theta,$$

and

(5.5.4) $$\mathbf{u} \times \mathbf{v} = (a_1 b_2 - a_2 b_1)\mathbf{k} = (|\mathbf{u}|\,|\mathbf{v}| \sin \theta)\mathbf{k},$$

where $\mathbf{k}$ is a unit vector perpendicular to the plane of $\mathbf{u}$ and $\mathbf{v}$.

Note that $\mathbf{u} \times \mathbf{v}$ is again a vector, whereas $\mathbf{u} \cdot \mathbf{v}$ is simply a scalar. The following results may be verified from the definitions of scalar and vector products:

(5.5.5) $$\mathbf{v} \cdot \mathbf{v} = |\mathbf{v}|^2,$$

(5.5.6) $$\mathbf{u} \cdot \mathbf{v} = \mathbf{v} \cdot \mathbf{u},$$

(5.5.7) $$\mathbf{u} \cdot (\mathbf{v} + \mathbf{w}) = \mathbf{u} \cdot \mathbf{v} + \mathbf{u} \cdot \mathbf{w},$$

(5.5.8) $$\mathbf{v} \times \mathbf{v} = \mathbf{0},$$

(5.5.9) $$\mathbf{u} \times \mathbf{v} = -\mathbf{v} \times \mathbf{u},$$

(5.5.10) $$\mathbf{u} \times (\mathbf{v} + \mathbf{w}) = \mathbf{u} \times \mathbf{v} + \mathbf{u} \times \mathbf{w}.$$

We conclude this section with a few remarks on the addition of vectors and two important results obtained therefrom.

The algebraic sum $\mathbf{u} + \mathbf{v}$ of the vectors $\mathbf{u} = (a_1, b_1)$ and $\mathbf{v} = (a_2, b_2)$ has been defined as the vector $(a_1 + a_2, b_1 + b_2)$. Geometrically, the addition of vectors follows the parallelogram law, that is, the sum $\mathbf{u} + \mathbf{v}$ of the vectors $\mathbf{u}$ and $\mathbf{v}$ is represented by the line segment joining the initial point of a representative of $\mathbf{u}$ to the terminal point of that representative of $\mathbf{v}$ whose initial point is at the terminal point of $\mathbf{u}$ (see Figure 5.7). In other words,

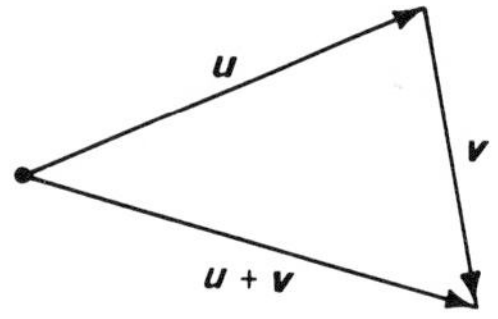

Figure 5.7

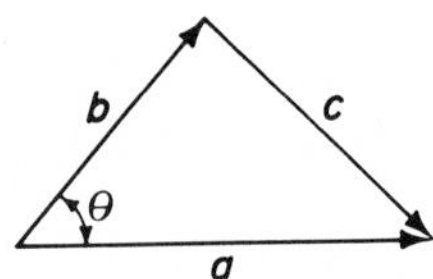

Figure 5.8

the vector $\mathbf{u} + \mathbf{v}$ is represented by the diagonal of the parallelogram with sides $\mathbf{u}$ and $\mathbf{v}$.

Now consider vectors $\mathbf{a}$, $\mathbf{b}$, and $\mathbf{c}$ in Figure 5.8. We have $\mathbf{b} + \mathbf{c} = \mathbf{a}$, that is,

$$\mathbf{c} = \mathbf{a} + (-\mathbf{b}) = \mathbf{a} - \mathbf{b}.$$

Then, using (5.5.7) and (5.5.6),

$$\begin{aligned} \mathbf{c} \cdot \mathbf{c} &= (\mathbf{a} - \mathbf{b}) \cdot (\mathbf{a} - \mathbf{b}) \\ &= \mathbf{a} \cdot \mathbf{a} + \mathbf{b} \cdot \mathbf{b} - 2\mathbf{a} \cdot \mathbf{b}. \end{aligned}$$

Hence, using (5.5.5) and (5.5.3), and setting $c = |\mathbf{c}|$, etc.,

$$c^2 = a^2 + b^2 - 2ab \cos \theta.$$

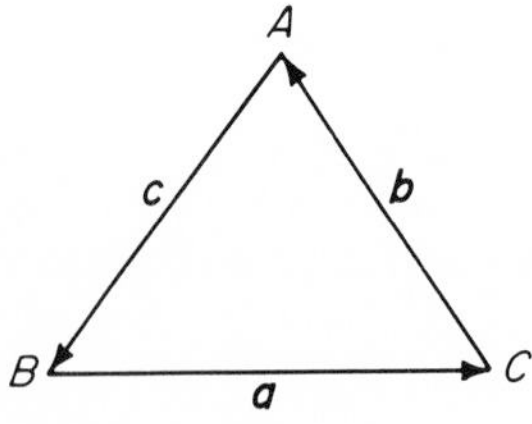

Figure 5.9

This, of course, is the familiar cosine law of trigonometry.

Finally, consider the vectors $\mathbf{a}$, $\mathbf{b}$, and $\mathbf{c}$ of Figure 5.9. We have

$$\mathbf{a} + \mathbf{b} + \mathbf{c} = 0;$$

so that

$$\begin{aligned} \mathbf{a} \times (\mathbf{a} + \mathbf{b} + \mathbf{c}) &= \mathbf{0}; \\ \mathbf{b} \times (\mathbf{a} + \mathbf{b} + \mathbf{c}) &= \mathbf{0}. \end{aligned}$$

The first of these relations yields

$$\mathbf{a} \times \mathbf{a} + \mathbf{a} \times \mathbf{b} + \mathbf{a} \times \mathbf{c} = \mathbf{0},$$

that is,

$$\mathbf{a} \times \mathbf{b} = -\mathbf{a} \times \mathbf{c} = \mathbf{c} \times \mathbf{a}.$$

Similarly, the second relation yields

$$\mathbf{b} \times \mathbf{c} = -\mathbf{b} \times \mathbf{a} = \mathbf{a} \times \mathbf{b};$$

hence

$$\mathbf{a} \times \mathbf{b} = \mathbf{b} \times \mathbf{c} = \mathbf{c} \times \mathbf{a}.$$

Equating the magnitudes of these vectors we have

$$ab \sin C = bc \sin A = ca \sin B,$$

that is,

$$\frac{\sin C}{c} = \frac{\sin A}{a} = \frac{\sin B}{b}$$

(assuming a, b, and c are all different from zero), and this result is the familiar sine law of trigonometry.

Vector algebra can also be applied in spherical trigonometry and plane geometry to prove many results and develop many formulae. Its main importance in geometry is the fact that this application can be generalized to 3-dimensional and even n-dimensional geometry.

EXERCISES

1. On a diagram, draw several *representatives of* the vectors (a) (2, 4), (b) (1, 2), (c) (−2, −1), (d) (0, 3), (e) (12, −5), (f) (−3, −5), (g) (6, 10).
2. Find the lengths of the vectors in Exercise 1.
3. Find unit vectors with the same direction as the vectors in Exercise 1.
4. Find the direction cosines of the vectors in Exercise 1. Which vectors have the same direction cosines?
5. (a) Considering the vectors $\boldsymbol{\epsilon}_\theta$ and $\boldsymbol{\epsilon}_{[(\pi/2)-\theta]}$ obtain the formulae

$$\sin\left(\frac{\pi}{2} - \theta\right) = \cos\theta; \qquad \cos\left(\frac{\pi}{2} - \theta\right) = \sin\theta.$$

   (b) Obtain similar formulae by considering (i) $\boldsymbol{\epsilon}_\theta$ and $\boldsymbol{\epsilon}_{[\pi/2+\theta]}$; (ii) $\boldsymbol{\epsilon}_\theta$ and $\boldsymbol{\epsilon}_{\pi-\theta}$; (iii) $\boldsymbol{\epsilon}_\theta$ and $\boldsymbol{\epsilon}_{\pi+\theta}$.
6. Verify (5.5.2) algebraically from (5.5.1).
7. (a) Find the scalar product and the magnitude of the vector products of the following pairs of vectors:
   (i) (2, −1), (6, −5); (ii) (2, −1), (1, 2);
   (iii) (3, −4), (4, −3); (iv) (5, 7), (−4, 0).

   (b) Which of the pairs of vectors in (i)–(iv) have the same direction, and which are at right angles to each other?
8. Verify (5.5.5)–(5.5.10).
9. Prove that the magnitude of $\mathbf{u} \times \mathbf{v}$ is twice the area of a triangle having $\mathbf{u}$ and $\mathbf{v}$ as two of its sides.

6

Numerical Analysis

by J. Wesley Graham

6.1. INTRODUCTION

D. R. Hartree, in his book *Numerical Analysis*, defines the subject as follows: "The subject of numerical analysis is concerned with the science and art of numerical calculation, and particularly with processes for getting certain kinds of numerical results from certain kinds of data".

For example, one may be required to solve several equations in as many unknowns, to find the roots of an equation in one unknown, to plot a curve, or perhaps to find the square root of two. Methods which can be used to solve these problems have been known for many years. However, when numerical results are required from more complicated formulae or systems of data, it is necessary to resort to more sophisticated methods. It is the aim of the mathematician working in Numerical Analysis to provide these methods.

Some of the techniques used to solve various problems are outlined in the following sections.

6.2. FINITE DIFFERENCES

Let us consider a function $f(x)$ evaluated for $x = 0, 1, 2, 3, 4$ (in general, we demand equally-spaced values for the independent variable x). We shall call the corresponding values of the function f_0, f_1, f_2, f_3, f_4. The data can then be arranged in a *finite difference table* (cf. Table 6.1).

The values for x and $f(x)$ are arranged in two vertical columns on the left. Then a column of "first differences" labelled $\Delta f(x)$ is obtained. The symbol Δ is merely an operator which signifies the operation of taking "first differences". The first difference symbol on the slanting line through $x = 0$ is called Δf_0, and is equal to $f_1 - f_0$. The symbol Δf_1 appears on the next line, and is equal to $f_2 - f_1$. Similar results hold for the whole first difference column; in general, $\Delta f_n = f_{n+1} - f_n$. The third column is headed by the symbol $\Delta^2 f(x)$, and contains second differences. The symbol which is on the first line is called $\Delta^2 f_0$, and is equal to $\Delta f_1 - \Delta f_0$. Thus, it is seen that the second differences are merely first differences of the $\Delta f(x)$ column. The column of third differences $\Delta^3 f(x)$ is obtained from the second difference column in a similar fashion. If more values of x and the function were available, we could consider further columns in the difference table.

Table 6.1. ORDINARY FINITE DIFFERENCE TABLE

x	$f(x)$	$\Delta f(x)$	$\Delta^2 f(x)$	$\Delta^3 f(x)$
0	f_0			
		$\Delta f_0 = f_1 - f_0$		
1	f_1		$\Delta^2 f_0 = \Delta f_1 - \Delta f_0$	
		$\Delta f_1 = f_2 - f_1$		$\Delta^3 f_0 = \Delta^2 f_1 - \Delta^2 f_0$
2	f_2		$\Delta^2 f_1 = \Delta f_2 - \Delta f_1$	
		$\Delta f_2 = f_3 - f_2$		$\Delta^3 f_1 = \Delta^2 f_2 - \Delta^2 f_1$
3	f_3		$\Delta^2 f_2 = \Delta f_3 - \Delta f_2$	
		$\Delta f_3 = f_4 - f_3$		
4	f_4			

Example 6.2.1. Construct a finite difference table for the function

$$f(x) = x^2 + 2x - 3$$

using values $x = 0, 1, 2, 3, 4, 5$.

Table 6.2. FINITE DIFFERENCE TABLE FOR $f(x) = x^2 + 2x - 3$

x	$f(x)$	$\Delta f(x)$	$\Delta^2 f(x)$	$\Delta^3 f(x)$
0	-3			
		3		
1	0		2	
		5		0
2	5		2	
		7		0
3	12		2	
		9		0
4	21		2	
		11		
5	32			

First of all, the function is evaluated for each of the values of x, and the table constructed according to the preceding rules. We are at once able to make some interesting observations. The column of second differences has a constant value 2, and consequently the third differences are all 0. This happens because we are dealing with a *second-degree* polynomial. If we had begun with a fifth-degree polynomial, then fifth differences would have been constant, and sixth differences would have vanished.

This observation can be summed up in the following theorem, which is easily proved by mathematical induction.

THEOREM 6.2.1. The nth differences for any polynomial of degree n are constant. Consequently, the $(n + 1)$th differences are zero.

In connection with the use of finite differences, Newton developed a very important formula which relates the values of $f(x)$ to the entries in the difference table. This is usually called *Newton's Advancing Difference Formula*

$$(6.2.1) \quad f(x) = f_0 + \frac{x}{1!}\Delta f_0 + \frac{x(x-1)}{2!}\Delta^2 f_0 + \frac{x(x-1)(x-2)}{3!}\Delta^3 f_0 + \cdots.$$

This formula has an infinite number of terms, but, for practical purposes, only the first few are necessary because high-order differences for polynomials eventually vanish (Theorem 6.2.1); if $f(x)$ is not a polynomial, Formula (6.2.1) still holds provided that the differences $\Delta^n f_0$ become small rapidly enough that the series on the right-hand side converges.

As an example, using the table developed for $f(x) = x^2 + 2x - 3$ (Table 6.2), we find that

$$f(2.5) = -3 + \frac{(2.5)3}{1!} + \frac{(2.5)(1.5)2}{2!} + \frac{(2.5)(1.5)(.5)0}{3!} = 8.25.$$

This result can readily be checked by substituting $x = 2.5$ in the function $x^2 + 2x - 3$.

This process of using Newton's Advancing Difference Formula (6.2.1) in conjunction with the difference table is called "interpolation", and one may justifiably ask the question: "Why go to the trouble of using a finite difference table and Newton's Formula when we can merely substitute in the expression defining the original function?". The answer is that, in actual practice, we often do not have the original function, or the function may not be readily computable by elementary methods.

Example 6.2.2. The following values of $10^5 \tan x$ were obtained from the Mathematical tables authorized by the Minister of Education for Ontario. Values are available for 6-minute intervals and are correct to

Table 6.3. VALUES OF THE FUNCTION $10^5 \tan x$

X	x	$10^5 \tan x$	Δ	Δ^2	Δ^3	Δ^4
0	80°	567128				
			5846			
1	80°6′	572974		118		
			5964		4	
2	80°12′	578938		122		0
			6086		4	
3	80°18′	585024		126		
			6212			
4	80°24′	591236				

five places of decimals (we use the function $10^5 \tan x$ in order to avoid using decimals in our work).

It is noted that third differences are constant, and consequently fourth differences are zero. This would lead us to assume that a polynomial of degree three represented these data, even though we know that the function is much more complicated, namely, $\tan x$. However, it is correct to say that a cubic polynomial represents $\tan x$ to about five places of decimals for x in the restricted region under consideration. We can then use Newton's Formula (6.2.1) to interpolate for other values of $\tan x$ not given in the table. However, the independent variable does not begin at zero and increase by unity each time; so a change of variable is necessary. Consider the new variable X given in the extreme left column of the table. It is easy to make the change from any value of x to the corresponding value of X and vice versa. Indeed, we see that

$$X = \frac{x - 80°}{6'} .$$

For example, if we require the tangent of 80°3′, then $x = 80°3'$ and $X = .5$. Consequently, we use $X = .5$ in Newton's Formula (6.2.1) as follows:

$$10^5 \tan 80°3' = 567128 + \frac{(.5)5846}{1!} + \frac{(.5)(-.5)118}{2!} + \frac{(.5)(-.5)(-1.5)4}{3!}$$
$$= 5700365.$$

Hence

$$\tan 80°3' = 5.70037.$$

It should be noted that this value for $\tan 80°3'$ is correct to five decimals (as can be checked from a larger table), and that, if we had used the common method of "linear interpolation", we should have obtained

$$\tan 80°3' = \tfrac{1}{2}(5.67128 + 5.72974) = 5.70051,$$

which is correct only to three decimals.

Newton's Advancing Difference Formula is only one of several numerical formulae used for interpolation. Some others are the Formulae of Gauss,

Bessel, Stirling, and Everett; each of these has its own particular advantages and uses.

6.3. NUMERICAL EVALUATION OF ROOTS OF EQUATIONS

The graph of a function $y = f(x)$ may cross the x-axis at various places; in Figure 6.1, $f(x)$ crosses the x-axis at two places A and B. These values of the variable x are the "real roots" of the equation $f(x) = 0$. There may be other values of x which satisfy $f(x) = 0$ and these would be complex roots, represented as $a + b\sqrt{-1}$, where a and b are real numbers. We will now consider two possible methods for obtaining real roots of equations.

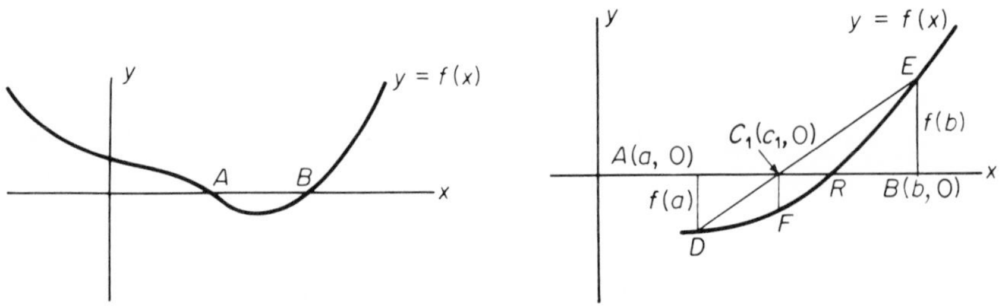

Figure 6.1 Figure 6.2

A very old method for determining a real root of the equation $f(x) = 0$ is the *regula falsi*. To apply this method, we find, by trial of various values, two values of x, say a and b, such that $f(a)$ is negative, $f(b)$ is positive, and $f(x)$ is continuous between a and b; let us assume $a < b$ (see Figure 6.2). Then we can consider the line DE, cutting the x-axis at the point $C_1(c_1, 0)$; c_1 will be nearer to the required root r than at least one of a or b. If $f(c_1)$ is negative, as it is in the diagram, then $f(c_1)$ is considered along with the positive value $f(b)$, and the line FE is drawn. This line then cuts the x-axis at a point C_2 still closer to $R(r, 0)$. This process is continued until the value of r is obtained to as many decimal places as required. The process of obtaining values of $c_1, c_2, c_3, \ldots$ which approach a required result r is called an *iterative procedure*; such a technique is common to many numerical methods.

The analytic expression for c_1 can be obtained from the similar triangles ADC_1 and BEC_1.

$$\frac{AD}{BE} = \frac{AC}{CB},$$

$$\frac{-f(a)}{f(b)} = \frac{c_1 - a}{b - c_1},$$

$$c_1 = \frac{a\,f(b) - b\,f(a)}{f(b) - f(a)}.$$

Example 6.3.1. Use the *regula falsi* to find a root of the equation

$$x^3 + 2x - 11 = 0.$$

Notice that $f(1) = -8, f(2) = +1$. Hence

$$c_1 = \frac{(1)(1) - (2)(-8)}{(1) - (-8)} \doteq 1.9.$$

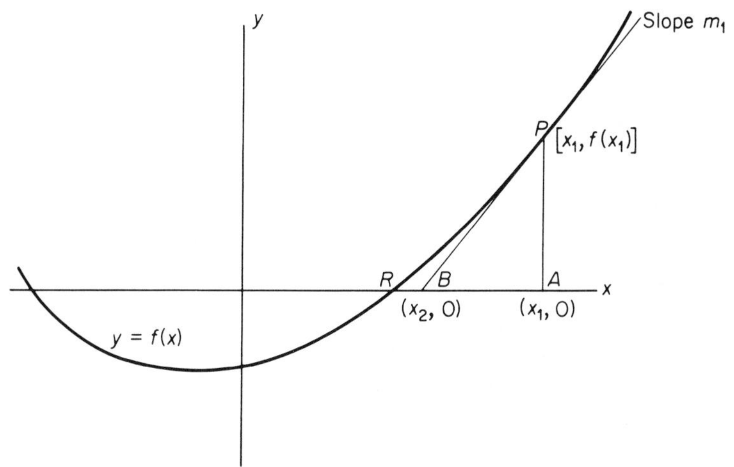

Figure 6.3

Then $f(1.9) = -.341, f(2) = +1$. Hence

$$c_2 = \frac{(1.9)(1) - (2)(-.341)}{1 - (-.341)} \doteq 1.925.$$

Then $f(1.925) = -.016672, f(2) = +1$. Hence

$$c_3 = \frac{(1.925)(1) - 2(-.016672)}{1 - (-.016672)} \doteq 1.926.$$

Hence we have the root $r = 1.93$ to two decimal places.

A second method of finding a real root r of the equation $f(x) = 0$ is *Newton's Method* (see Figure 6.3). We select a value x_1 near the root r, and calculate the value $f(x_1)$ of the function. At the point $P[x_1, f(x_1)]$, construct the tangent to the curve $y = f(x)$. It has slope m_1, and cuts the x-axis at the point $B(x_2, 0)$, which is closer to $R(r, 0)$ than was $A(x_1, 0)$. This process is repeated, starting from x_2, to provide a value x_3 which is even closer to r than x_1 or x_2. We continue this iterative procedure until we obtain x_n, an approximation to R containing as many decimal places as required.

The analytic expression for x_2 in terms of x_1 can be obtained by considering the triangle PAB.

$$\tan PBA = \frac{PA}{AB};$$

hence

$$m_1 = \frac{f(x_1)}{x_1 - x_2};$$

$$x_2 = x_1 - \frac{f(x_1)}{m_1}.$$

Now m_1 is given by calculus as $f'(x_1)$ [cf. Chapter 8 for the definition of the derivative $f'(x)$ of the function $f(x)$]. So

$$x_2 = x_1 - \frac{f(x_1)}{f'(x_1)}.$$

Similarly,

$$x_3 = x_2 - \frac{f(x_2)}{f'(x_2)},$$

and, in general,

$$x_{n+1} = x_n - \frac{f(x_n)}{f'(x_n)}.$$

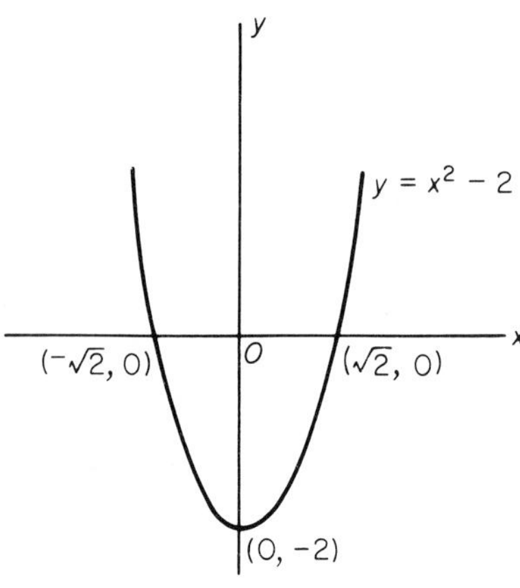

Figure 6.4

Example 6.3.2. Consider the function $y = x^2 - 2$, illustrated in Figure 6.4. It crosses the x-axis at the points $x = \pm\sqrt{2}$ (the solutions of the equation $x^2 - 2 = 0$). However, the symbol $\sqrt{2}$ is nothing more than a symbol, and, to perform numerical calculations, one must express $\sqrt{2}$ in decimal form as 1.4142135 . . . ; we can apply Newton's method as follows.

$$f(x) = x^2 - 2, \qquad f'(x) = 2x.$$

Then

$$x_2 = x_1 - \frac{(x_1^2 - 2)}{2x_1}.$$

This simplifies to

$$x_2 = \frac{1}{2}\left(x_1 + \frac{2}{x_1}\right)$$

To find $\sqrt{2}$, start from $x_1 = 1$; then

$$x_2 = \tfrac{1}{2}(1 + \tfrac{2}{1}) = 1.5,$$

$$x_3 = \tfrac{1}{2}(\tfrac{3}{2} + \tfrac{4}{3}) = \tfrac{17}{12} = 1.4166666,$$

$$x_4 = \tfrac{1}{2}(\tfrac{17}{12} + \tfrac{24}{17}) = 1.4142156,$$

$$x_5 = 1.4142135,$$

$$x_6 = 1.4142135.$$

Hence Newton's iterative procedure has produced the value $\sqrt{2}$ correct to at least six decimal places.

As a slightly more complicated illustration, let us consider

Example 6.3.3. Find the root near 2 of the equation

$$x^3 + 3x^2 - 3x - 12 = 0.$$

In this problem,

$$f(x) = x^3 + 3x^2 - 3x - 12,$$
$$f'(x) = 3x^2 + 6x - 3.$$

Start from $x_1 = 2$. Then

$$x_2 = 2 - \frac{f(2)}{f'(2)} = 2 - \frac{2}{21} \doteq 1.9.$$

$$\begin{aligned} x_3 &= 1.9 - \frac{f(1.9)}{f'(1.9)} \\ &= 1.9 - \frac{-.011}{19.23} \\ &= 1.9006. \end{aligned}$$

Complex roots occur when values such as $a + b\sqrt{-1}$ satisfy the equation $f(x) = 0$. These are often difficult to obtain; however, many methods are available, some of which use iterative processes to obtain results.

6.4. SOLUTIONS OF SYSTEMS OF LINEAR EQUATIONS BY THE METHOD OF RELAXATION

It is often necessary to solve large systems of linear equations in many unknowns. For example, it is not unusual, in a research or business problem, to require the solution of 100 equations in 100 unknowns. This is the type of problem that would not, in general, be solved manually. The usual method of pairing equations and eliminating one unknown at a time is straightforward, but, in general, an electronic computer would be required for such a large system of equations. In this section, we shall describe the *Method of Relaxation*, which is, under many circumstances, an excellent method for manual solution of small systems of linear equations. A similar relaxation procedure is used in other branches of numerical analysis as well. We start with two equations in two unknowns in order to simplify the computation and thereby illustrate the method more clearly.

Example 6.4.1. Solve the equations

$$\begin{aligned} 6x + y + 8 &= 0, \\ x + 9y + 9 &= 0. \end{aligned}$$

Consider the equations in the form

$$6x + y + 8 = R_1,$$

$$x + 9y + 9 = R_2.$$

Form an operations table (Table 6.4).

Table 6.4

Δx	Δy	ΔR_1	ΔR_2
1	0	6	1
0	1	1	9

The symbol Δx means "a change in the variable x". A similar interpretation is given to the symbols Δy, ΔR_1, ΔR_2. R_1 and R_2 are called *residuals*. Consider the first line in Table 6.4. It states that if we change x by one unit and do not change y, then R_1 changes by six units and R_2 changes by one unit. The second line of the operations table states that if we do not change x at all, and if we change y by one unit, then R_1 changes by one unit and R_2 by nine units.

Table 6.5

Step I

$x = 0$	$y = 0$	$R_1 = 8$	$R_2 = 9$
0	−1	7	0
−1	0	1	−1
−1	−1	1	−1

If we can find values of x and y such that $R_1 = R_2 = 0$, these values will be the required solution. We can begin by guessing that $x = y = 0$ is the solution; we note that $R_1 = 8$ and $R_2 = 9$. We look in Table 6.4, and note that, if we change y by -1, then R_2 would change by -9 (and thus become zero). At the same time, R_1 changes from 8 to 7. Then we note that R_1, now equal to 7, can be reduced to 1 if we change x by -1. At the same time, we change R_2 to -1.

Our work so far can be summarized in Table 6.5.

The last line can be checked by substitution in the given equations; it states that if $x = -1$, $y = -1$, then the values of R_1 and R_2 are 1 and -1 respectively.

Now, in order to avoid using decimals, we multiply the last line of Table 6.5 by 10 before starting the second step in the relaxation. Then we are building up the answer $10x$ and $10y$, rather than x and y. The second and subsequent steps continue in like manner.

Table 6.6

Step II

−10	−10	10	−10
0	1	11	−1
−2	0	−1	−3
−12	−9	−1	−3

Step III

−120	−90	−10	−30
0	3	−7	−3
1	0	−1	−2
−119	−87	−1	−2

Step IV

−1190	−870	−10	−20
0	2	−8	−2
1	0	−2	−1
−1189	−868	−2	−1

Step V

−11890	−8680	−20	−10
0	1	−19	−1
3	0	−1	2
−11887	−8679	−1	2

We have thus reached the result that

$$10^4x = -11887, \qquad 10^4y = -8679,$$

is a solution such that

$$10^4R_1 = -1, \qquad 10^4R_2 = 2.$$

Hence

$$x = -1.1887, \qquad y = -.8679,$$

makes

$$R_1 = -.0001, \qquad R_2 = .0002.$$

We note that, at each step of the relaxation, one decimal place is added to the result. This, however, is not always the case, since some sets of equations are very "ill-conditioned". This situation arises when two or more equations in the set are almost identical. For example, the problem we have just used as an illustration would not have worked out so well if the equations had represented two lines that were very close to one another (intersected at a very small angle).

Example 6.4.2. Use relaxation to solve the equations

$$\begin{aligned} 2x - 4y + 17z - 13 &= 0, \\ 15x + y - 3z + 11 &= 0, \\ 3x + 21y + 2z - 5 &= 0. \end{aligned}$$

Consider the equations in the form

$$\begin{aligned} 2x - 4y + 17z - 13 &= R_1, \\ 15x + y - 3z + 11 &= R_2, \\ 3x + 21y + 2z - 5 &= R_3. \end{aligned}$$

Form an operations table (Table 6.7).

Table 6.7

Δx	Δy	Δz	ΔR_1	ΔR_2	ΔR_3
1	0	0	2	15	3
0	1	0	−4	1	21
0	0	1	17	−3	2

The steps in the relaxation proceed as in Example 6.4.1.

Step I

$x = 0$	$y = 0$	$z = 0$	$R_1 = -13$	$R_2 = 11$	$R_3 = -5$
0	0	1	4	8	−3
0	0	1	4	8	−3

Step II

0	0	10	40	80	−30
−5	0	0	30	5	−45
0	2	0	22	7	−3
0	0	−1	5	10	−5
−5	2	9	5	10	−5

Step III

−50	20	90	50	100	−50
−7	0	0	36	−5	−71
0	3	0	24	−2	−8
0	0	−1	7	1	−10
−57	23	89	7	1	−10

Step IV

−570	230	890	70	10	−100
0	5	0	50	15	5
0	0	−3	−1	24	−1
−1	0	0	−3	9	−4
−571	235	887	−3	9	−4

Step V

−5710	2350	8870	−30	90	−40
−6	0	0	−42	0	−58
0	3	0	−54	3	5
0	0	3	−3	−6	11
−5716	2353	8873	−3	−6	11

We conclude that

$$10^4x = -5716, \qquad x = -.5716;$$
$$10^4y = 2353, \qquad y = +.2353;$$
$$10^4z = 8873, \qquad z = +.8873.$$

EXERCISES

1. Construct a finite difference table for the function
$$f(x) = x^3 + 2x^2 - 6x + 9$$
when $x = 0, 1, 2, 3, 4, 5$. Use Newton's Advancing Difference Formula to calculate $f(2.12)$.

2. In Example 6.2.2 a table for $10^5 \tan x$ was constructed for x having values between 80° and 80°24′, at intervals of 6′. Use this table and Newton's Advancing Difference Formula to find (a) tan 80°7′, (b) tan 80°10′. Compare your results with those obtained using linear interpolation.

3. Use the *regula falsi* to show that 2.75 is a root, correct to two decimal places, of the equation $x^3 - 5x - 7 = 0$.

4. Use the *regula falsi* to solve the equation $x^2 - 3 = 0$, thereby obtaining $\sqrt{3}$ to two decimals.

5. Newton's Method can be used to find the cube root of any number N by iteration. The iterative formula is

$$x_2 = \frac{1}{3}\left[2x_1 + \frac{N}{x_1^2}\right].$$

Use this formula to calculate $\sqrt[3]{2}$ to six decimals. (Start with $x_1 = 1$.)

6. Newton's Method could be used to solve for the root in Exercise 3. The iterative formula is

$$x_2 = x_1 - \frac{x_1^3 - 5x_1 - 7}{3x_1^2 - 5}.$$

With a starting value $x_1 = 2$, show that, with only two applications of the above formula, we obtain $r = 2.75$ (correct to two decimals).

7. Use the method of relaxation to solve the following systems of equations.

(a)
$$\begin{aligned} 14x - y &= 12, \\ 2x + 12y &= 9, \end{aligned}$$

(b)
$$\begin{aligned} x + 13y + 2z &= 20, \\ 3x - y + 18z &= 14, \\ 11x + 2y - z &= -13. \end{aligned}$$

7

Functions of a Single Variable

by Ralph G. Stanton

7.1. DEFINITION AND EXAMPLES

If a certain quantity, say x, may assume arbitrary values chosen from a set R of numbers, then we refer to x as an *independent variable*. Usually, in elementary work, x may assume only real values; we then refer to x as a real independent variable, or simply as a *real variable*. If no contrary information is given, we shall always consider the independent variable x as a real independent variable; if x is restricted in any way, the information is usually supplied by giving an interval in which x may or may not lie. For example,

$x > 4$: x is any real number greater than 4;

$x \neq 0$: x is any real number different from zero;

$|x| \geq 1$: x is any real number greater than or equal to 1; or less than or equal to -1;

$x > 0$, x rational: x is any positive rational number.

Of course, any symbol may be employed to denote the independent variable; x is not sacrosanct, merely very common.

If a second quantity y is such that, given any value of x, there is exactly one value determined for the quantity y, then we say that y is a *dependent variable;* we further state that *y is a function of x.* The values of y will range over a set of numbers; in elementary work, we frequently restrict these values to the set of real numbers.

Note. At this stage, we will digress for a short space in order to explain a terminology which the reader may have encountered in other places. In the past, it has been very common to define a *multiple-valued function* in the following way: If a quantity y is such that, given any value of x, we are able to ascertain a set of c values for the quantity y (where c may differ for differing values of x), then we say that y is a dependent variable and state that y is a c-valued function of x.

When one uses multiple-valued functions, ambiguities arise, and one has to be very careful to distinguish which of the set of functional values is being referred to at any time; for this reason, it is becoming usual to restrict the word *function* to mean a *single-valued function.* However, one still finds multiple-valued functions frequently used in elementary calculus texts, in works on complex variables (where one goes to great trouble to make functions single-valued by constructing Riemann surfaces), in older reference works, and in some current periodicals. Consequently, the reader should be aware that, while the word *function* generally implies a single-valued function, some authors do employ the word in a broader sense. In this chapter, we shall, unless otherwise specifically stated, use the word *function* interchangeably with the phrase *single-valued function*, where the adjective is merely employed to add emphasis.

Example 7.1.1

$$y = x^2 - 2x - 13$$

Since no restriction is given, we take x as an arbitrary real number; then, given any value for x, we can compute exactly one value for y (and this value will be a real number greater than or equal to -14). Hence, in this example, we say that *y is a single-valued function of x.*

Example 7.1.2. Let b be the base of a rectangle inscribed in a circle of radius 5. Then b is an independent variable capable of assuming any real value in the range from zero to ten. It is easy to show that, if A denotes the area of the rectangle, then

$$A = b\sqrt{100 - b^2},$$

where $0 \leq b \leq 10$.

In this illustration, the physical nature of the problem imposed a natural restriction on the domain of the independent variable b.

Example 7.1.3. Let r and h be the base radius and the height, respectively, of a cone. Then it is a well-known result of mensuration that

$$V = \tfrac{1}{3}\pi r^2 h,$$

where V is the volume of the cone.

In this case, V is a function of the *two* independent variables r and h; physical considerations ensure that $0 \leq r$, and that $0 \leq h$. Then, if we know *both r and h*, we can compute the value of the dependent variable V.

Example 7.1.4

$$y^2 = x, \qquad x \geq 0.$$

Here we notice that, for $x = 0$, then $y = 0$, and y is a single-valued function of x; however, for any $x > 0$, we see that $y = \pm\sqrt{x}$, that is, a knowledge of x enables us to compute two values of y. (We recall that $\sqrt{x}$, by convention, refers only to the positive square root of x.)

Example 7.1.5. Consider the relation

$$y = x^2 - 2x - 13,$$

given that y is the real independent variable. By writing

$$y = (x - 1)^2 - 14,$$

we see that, for x to be real, y must be restricted to lie in the range $y \geq -14$; also

$$x = 1 \pm \sqrt{y + 14}.$$

So, the relation

$$y = x^2 - 2x - 13$$

defines y as a single-valued function of x (Example 7.1.1); however, for $y > -14$, two values of x are determined when any value of y is assigned ($y = -14$ determines a single value of x).

Example 7.1.5 illustrates the fact that there is no way of looking at a relationship such as

$$y = x^2 - 2x - 13$$

and determining which variable is the independent variable; the independent variable is that variable to which we assign values; indeed, we might even call it the *first* variable and call the dependent variable the *second* variable. In general, which variable is independent is a subjective matter which is determined by the mathematician.

As we have previously stated, many contemporary authors restrict the term function to mean single-valued function; this is a convention which may or may not be used in any particular book.

Example 7.1.6

$$y = x\sqrt{x - 3}.$$

Here, y is defined as a single-valued function of x. We see that, in order to keep y real, it is necessary to restrict x. So, we say that y is defined as a real function of x for $x = 0$ and for $x \geq 3$.

It is worth noticing that the rule

$$y = x\sqrt{x - 3}$$

does not determine the same set of pairings (x, y) as is determined by the rule

$$y^2 = x^2(x - 3).$$

This latter relationship does determine a single value of y for $x = 0$ or for $x = 3$; for $x > 3$, assignment of a value to x determines two values for y. Later on (cf. Example 7.9.1), we shall see that there are exactly two continuous single-valued functions which satisfy the relationship

$$y^2 = x^2(x - 3);$$

these are given by the rules $y = x\sqrt{x - 3}$ and $y = -x\sqrt{x - 3}$.

Example 7.1.7. Consider $y = \sqrt{25 - x^2}$ as a real function of the real variable x.

Since y is to be real, there is a natural restriction that x lie in the range $-5 \leq x \leq 5$; for x in this range, y is defined as a *positive single-valued* function of x.

7.2. WHAT IS A FUNCTION?

So far, we have not explained what a function is; rather, we have spoken of one quantity's "being a function of" another quantity. And it is really the relationship of "being a function of" which is important; when we attempt to pinpoint just what a function is, we run into philosophic and subjective difficulties.

One way of looking at a function is to define the function as "the collection of all ordered pairs (x_i, y_i) with the property that, for any arbitrary x value, we are given some means of computing the corresponding y value(s)". For example, if we are given that x and y are to be real numbers, and that they are connected by the rule

$$y = 4x - 5,$$

then the function is defined as the infinite set of number pairs such as $(1, -1)$, $(2, 3)$, $(-4, -21)$, $(0, -5)$, $(\frac{1}{2}, -3)$, etc.

A second way of looking at a function is to say that "a function is defined by stating the range for x, the range for y, and the rule which associates a y

value with any x value". Since we have agreed that, unless otherwise stated, the range for x and the range for y are to be real, we see that a rule such as

$$y = 4x - 5$$

determines y as a function of x. In this "rule" way of looking at a function, we are really writing down a typical or representative number pair $(x, 4x - 5)$ from the infinite set of such pairs.

Both of the preceding ways of looking at functions are somewhat passive, in that we regard the function as a collection of number pairs. The collection is given potentially or completely, depending on whether or not we write down a representative generic pair. However, we can give a more active definition in the following way. Suppose that, for example, the y values are determined by the rule

$$y = x^2 - 2x + 7.$$

Such an algebraic relationship allows the y value to be computed for any arbitrary x value. Then we consider that a function f is determined, where f is the linkage, or correspondence, or mapping, which associates with every x value a corresponding y value. Thus, if we use an arrow to denote correspondence, we have

$$3 \longrightarrow 10,$$

$$-2 \longrightarrow 15,$$

$$a \longrightarrow a^2 - 2a + 7.$$

The function f is then the active principle of correspondence which associates with the number 3 a second number (or "image"), namely, 10; in general, f takes the number a and determines for it a correspondent, namely, $a^2 - 2a + 7$.

A development of the last paragraph gives us what is probably the most fruitful philosophic way of looking at a function. As always, we agree that the ranges of x and of y are specified. Then a function f is an operator which changes any assigned x value into a corresponding y value. Using a rough analogy, we can think of f as a distorting mirror at a country fair; the value of x is the "object" on which the mirror acts, and the value of y is the "image" which appears after f has acted upon x. Thus, if f is defined by the rule

$$f(x) = x^3 - 7x + 4,$$

we see that f takes the number 2 and operates upon it to produce the number -2. We write $f(2) = -2$. Similarly, $f(4) = 40$. And, in general, a real number a, when "distorted" or acted upon by the operator f, becomes

$$f(a) = a^3 - 7a + 4.$$

Naturally, all these ways of looking at the functional concept are equivalent. When we are given the function defined by the rule

$$y = x^3,$$

we may think of it as comprising all ordered pairs like

$$(0, 0); \quad (1, 1); \quad (2, 8); \quad (1.2, 1.728); \quad (-.3, -.027); \quad \ldots .$$

Or we may think of the function as the set of all pairs of the generic form (x, x^3). Or we may think of the function as the mapping f which carries x into x^3 according to the correspondence

$$x \xrightarrow{f} x^3.$$

Or finally we may think of the function f as an operator which actually changes x into an "image" x^3, that is, $f(x) = x^3$; in short, f operating upon x produces x^3.

In any case, the important thing is to realize what we mean by the phrase "y is a function of x", namely, that, for x given a permissible value, we can compute y.

Those writers who use the term function to mean "single-valued function" think of a function as a "collection of all ordered pairs (x_i, y_i) with the property that, for an arbitrary x value, we are given some way of computing *exactly one* corresponding y value". Thus, they permit

$$y = x^3$$

to define y as a function of x, but deny that the rule

$$x^2 + 2y^2 = 9$$

defines y as a function of x. On a broader interpretation, this last relation would comprise all number "pairings" of the form

$$(3, 0); \quad (-3, 0); \quad (2, \sqrt{2.5}); \quad (2, -\sqrt{2.5}); \quad (1, 2); \quad (1, -2); \quad \ldots .$$

More generally, we might write these "pairings" as

$$(3, 0); \quad (-3, 0); \quad (2; +\sqrt{2.5}, -\sqrt{2.5}); \quad (1; 2, -2); \quad \ldots .$$

where we allow a double y-value to correspond to some x values.

7.3. FUNCTIONAL NOTATION

Two common notations for functions are exemplified by the rules

$$y = x^2 - 5x + 1 \quad \text{and} \quad f(x) = x^2 - 5x + 1.$$

In each case, the function defined is the same; the only difference is that the dependent variable is named y in the first case and $f(x)$ in the second. However, the function comprises all pairings such as

$$(1, -3); \quad (0, 1); \quad (-3, 25); \quad \ldots .$$

The second notation is often more convenient since, if we wish to specify a functional value, we may say

$$\text{When} \quad x = 4, \quad \text{then} \quad y = -3,$$

or simply

$$f(4) = -3.$$

Certainly the statement $f(4) = -3$ is the more concise way of specifying the y value corresponding to 4.

Example 7.3.1. Given $f(x) = (2x + 5)/(3 - 2x)$, compute $f(0)$, $f(1)$, $f(a), f(-x), f(1 - x), f(x^{-1})$, $[f(x)]^{-1}, f[f(x)]$.

We immediately find the following results.

$$f(0) = \tfrac{5}{3}; \quad f(1) = 7;$$

$$f(a) = \frac{2a + 5}{3 - 2a}; \quad f(-x) = \frac{5 - 2x}{3 + 2x};$$

$$f(1 - x) = \frac{2(1 - x) + 5}{3 - 2(1 - x)} = \frac{7 - 2x}{1 + 2x};$$

$$f(x^{-1}) = \frac{2x^{-1} + 5}{3 - 2x^{-1}} = \frac{2 + 5x}{3x - 2};$$

$$[f(x)]^{-1} = \frac{3 - 2x}{2x + 5};$$

$$f[f(x)] = \frac{2f(x) + 5}{3 - 2f(x)} = \frac{6x - 25}{10x + 1}.$$

Sometimes the restriction of x and $f(x)$ to real values causes two functions, which appear superficially the same, to be different. Thus, if

$$f(x) = 2x,$$

with x a real variable, the function comprises all number pairs of the form (2, 4); (—3, —6); et cetera. On the other hand, the function

$$g(x) = \sin(\sin^{-1} 2x)$$

differs from $f(x) = 2x$ in virtue of the fact that, as long as we permit only real values, $g(x)$ is a sine function and so can vary only between -1 and $+1$. Hence $g(x)$ is defined only for $-\frac{1}{2} \le x \le \frac{1}{2}$, and we see that $g(x) = f(x)$ throughout this common range of definition. On the other hand, for $|x| > \frac{1}{2}$, $f(x)$ is still defined, but $g(x)$ is not defined.

It would be appropriate to conclude this section by remarking on the distinction between a function and its functional values. Suppose $y = f(x)$ represents a given function. Then:

$f(2)$ is the functional value when the independent variable assumes the value 2,
$f(a)$ is the functional value when the independent variable assumes the value a,
$f(x)$ is the functional value when the independent variable assumes the value x.

We sometimes also speak of "the function $f(x)$", meaning thereby simply "the function represented by the relation $y = f(x)$" or "the function comprising all pairs $[x, f(x)]$". This convention provides brevity.

EXERCISES

1. Find the range of x for which the following relations determine y as a real function of x:

   (a) $y = \cos^{-1} x$, (b) $y = \log(x + 5)$, (c) $y = \sqrt{x - 4}$.

2. If $f(x) = \cos x$, evaluate
$$f(2x) - [f(x)]^2 + [f(\tfrac{1}{2}\pi - x)]^2.$$

3. If $f(x) = 2^x$, $g(x) = \log_2(x)$, evalutate
$$f[g(x)] - 2g[f(x)].$$

4. If $f(x) = (ax + b)/(cx - a)$, evaluate
$$f(x^2),\quad [f(x)]^2,\quad f(x^{-1}),\quad [f(x)]^{-1},\quad f(x - a),\quad f[f(x)].$$

5. If $f(x) = x^2 - 2x + 5$, evaluate
$$f(a) + f(a - x) + f(x - a).$$

6. If $f(x) = 1 - 3^x$, evaluate
$$\frac{f(3x)}{f(x)} + f(x) + f(2x).$$

7. If $f(x) = 3^x + 3^{-x}$, evaluate
$$f(a) + f(b) + f(a - b) + f(a + b) - f(a)f(b).$$

8. If $f(x) = (2^x - 2^{-x})/(2^x + 2^{-x})$, evaluate
$$f(2x) - 2f(x) + f(2x)[f(x)]^2.$$

9. If $f(x) = x - x^{-1}$, evaluate
$$[f(x)]^4 - [f(x^2)]^2 + 4[f(x)]^2.$$

10. If $g(x) = 2(3^x - 3^{-x})^{-1}$, evaluate

$$\frac{[g(x)]^3}{g(3x)} - 3[g(x)]^2.$$

11. If $g(x) = 3^x - 3^{-x}$, evaluate

$$\left\{\frac{g(3x)}{g(x)} - [g(x)]^2\right\}^{-1}.$$

12. Let $f(x) = 2x^2 - 1$, $g(x) = \cos(2\cos^{-1} x)$. Show that

$$f(x) = g(x) \qquad \text{if} \qquad -1 \leq x \leq 1.$$

Show that the functions differ by considering $f(2)$ and $g(2)$.

7.4. LIMITS

The concept of limit will be discussed at greater length in the next chapter; here, we shall introduce the concept only insofar as it is required for the purpose of considering graphs of functions.

Let us, for example, consider a function such as

$$y = x^2 - x + 4;$$

it is clear that, if x is assigned a value very very close to 3, then y assumes a value very close to 10. In short, if x is *arbitrarily close* (or as close as we please) to 3, then y is *arbitrarily close* to 10. We also say "The limit of y, as x approaches 3, is 10". Or we write: "As $x \longrightarrow 3$, $y \longrightarrow 10$".

We may then make the following

DEFINITION. If $y = f(x)$ is a given single-valued function, and if, as x gets arbitrarily close to a number a, then y gets arbitrarily close to a number b, we say that *the limit of y, as x approaches a, is b.* We write

$$\lim_{x \to a} y = b$$

as an abbreviation of this statement.

Example 7.4.1. Let $f(x) = x^2 + 3x$; then

$$\lim_{x \to -5} f(x) = 10.$$

This means that we can find a value $f(x)$ arbitrarily close to 10 by taking x arbitrarily close to -5. For example, let us suppose we wish to have $f(x)$ within ϵ units of 10 (ϵ a real positive number, say $\epsilon < \frac{1}{2}$). Let us take a value of $x = -5 \pm \delta$, where δ is also a real positive number. Then

$$10 - \epsilon \leq f(-5 \pm \delta) \leq 10 + \epsilon,$$

that is, we demand that δ be chosen small enough so as to make $f(-5 \pm \delta)$ lie within ϵ units of 10. Clearly,

$$10 - \epsilon \leq 10 \mp 7\delta + \delta^2 \leq 10 + \epsilon;$$
$$-\epsilon \leq \delta^2 \mp 7\delta \leq \epsilon.$$

Now if δ is taken less than $\epsilon/10$, we see that (using $\epsilon < \frac{1}{2}$)

$$|\delta^2 + 7\delta| < \left|\frac{\epsilon^2}{100} + \frac{7\epsilon}{10}\right| < \left|\frac{\epsilon}{200} + \frac{7\epsilon}{10}\right| < \epsilon;$$

also
$$|\delta^2 - 7\delta| < |-7\delta| < \left|\frac{7\epsilon}{10}\right| < \epsilon.$$

Consequently, for $\epsilon < \frac{1}{2}$, $\delta = \epsilon/10$ will ensure that if x is within δ units of -5, then $f(x)$ is within ϵ units of 10. This is just a fancy way of saying that $f(x)$ *can be made arbitrarily close to 10 by taking x sufficiently close to -5.*

The definition of a limit can be given formally in terms of δ and ϵ by saying: "If $y = f(x)$ is a given single-valued function, and if for any given real $\epsilon > 0$ we can find a corresponding $\delta > 0$ such that, whenever

$$|x - a| < \delta,$$

then $|y - b| < \epsilon$, we say that the limit of y, as x approaches a, is b, and write

$$\lim_{x\to a} y = b\text{''}.$$

Note that what happens if x is set equal to a is completely irrelevant to the value of

$$\lim_{x\to a} y.$$

Example 7.4.2. Evaluate $\lim\limits_{x\to 2} (x^2 - 3x + 2)/(x^3 - 8)$.

Here

$$\lim_{x\to 2} \frac{x^2 - 3x + 2}{x^3 - 8} = \lim_{x\to 2} \frac{(x-2)(x-1)}{(x-2)(x^2+2x+4)}.$$

Now, as x assumes a value very close to 2, $x - 2$ is certainly a very small number; but this same very small number occurs in both numerator and denominator, and, even if it were 10^{-6}, cancels out. Thus

$$\lim_{x\to 2} \frac{x^2 - 3x + 2}{x^3 - 8} = \lim_{x\to 2} \frac{x - 1}{x^2 + 2x + 4},$$

and, from this latter form, it is clear (since $x - 1$ approaches 1 and $x^2 + 2x + 4$ approaches 12 as x gets arbitrarily close to 2) that

$$\lim_{x\to 2} \frac{x^2 - 3x + 2}{x^3 - 8} = \frac{1}{12}.$$

For example, if $x = 2.0001$, then

$$\frac{x^2 - 3x + 2}{x^3 - 8} = \frac{(x-2)(x-1)}{(x-2)(x^2+2x+4)}$$

$$= \frac{(.0001)(1.0001)}{(.0001)(12.00060001)}$$

$$= \frac{1.0001}{12.00060001},$$

and this result is very close to $\frac{1}{12}$.

Example 7.4.3. Evaluate $\lim_{h \to 0} (\sqrt{6+h} - \sqrt{6})/h$.

Here we write

$$\lim_{h\to 0} \frac{\sqrt{6+h} - \sqrt{6}}{h} = \lim_{h\to 0} \frac{\sqrt{6+h} - \sqrt{6}}{h} \frac{\sqrt{6+h} + \sqrt{6}}{\sqrt{6+h} + \sqrt{6}}$$

$$= \lim_{h\to 0} \frac{h}{h(\sqrt{6+h} + \sqrt{6})}$$

$$= \lim_{h\to 0} \frac{1}{\sqrt{6+h} + \sqrt{6}}$$

$$= \frac{1}{2\sqrt{6}}.$$

The presence of a literal value in an expression does not affect the operation of taking the limit. For instance

Example 7.4.4. Evaluate $\lim_{h \to 0} (\sqrt{2x+h} - \sqrt{2x})/h$.

Here h must assume values arbitrarily close to zero; x is fixed. So,

$$\lim_{h\to 0} \frac{\sqrt{2x+h} - \sqrt{2x}}{h} = \lim_{h\to 0} \frac{\sqrt{2x+h} - \sqrt{2x}}{h} \frac{\sqrt{2x+h} + \sqrt{2x}}{\sqrt{2x+h} + \sqrt{2x}}$$

$$= \lim_{h\to 0} \frac{h}{h(\sqrt{2x+h} + \sqrt{2x})}$$

$$= \lim_{h\to 0} \frac{1}{\sqrt{2x+h} + \sqrt{2x}}$$

$$= \frac{1}{2\sqrt{2x}}.$$

We must now underline a fundamental distinction; if $y = f(x)$ is a given function, there is no necessary connection between

$$\lim_{x \to a} f(x)$$

and the value $f(a)$. The latter can also be denoted by "the value of $f(x)$, when x is set equal to a, that is,

$$\operatorname*{Value}_{x=a} f(x),$$

or simply,

$$f(x)\Big|_{x=a}\text{''}.$$

For

$$\lim_{x \to a} f(x)$$

depends only on the behaviour of $f(x)$ as x gets arbitrarily close to a. And $f(a)$ depends on what happens to $f(x)$ when x is set equal to a. A few illustrations will show that these two quantities may differ.

Example 7.4.5

$$f(x) = x^2, \qquad a = 2.$$

Clearly, as x gets arbitrarily close to 2, $f(x)$ gets arbitrarily close to 4. So

$$\lim_{x \to 2} f(x) = 4,$$

and this also happens to be the value $f(2)$.

Example 7.4.6

$$f(x) = \frac{x^2 - 49}{x^2 - 9x + 14}, \qquad a = 7.$$

Here

$$\begin{aligned}\lim_{x \to 7} f(x) &= \lim_{x \to 7} \frac{(x - 7)(x + 7)}{(x - 7)(x + 2)}\\ &= \lim_{x \to 7} \frac{x + 7}{x + 2}\\ &= \frac{14}{9}.\end{aligned}$$

However,

$$f(7) = \tfrac{0}{0};$$

in the next section, we shall show that $\frac{0}{0}$ can have no meaning; at the moment it suffices to notice that it certainly differs from the quantity $\frac{14}{9}$.

Example 7.4.7. Consider

$$f(x) = \frac{x^2}{1 + x^2} + \frac{x^2}{(1 + x^2)^2} + \frac{x^2}{(1 + x^2)^3} + \cdots,$$

and let us take $a = 0$. Certainly $f(0) = 0$; on the other hand, if $x \neq 0$, then

$$1 + x^2 > 1,$$

and so the infinite geometric series sums to

$$\begin{aligned} f(x) &= \frac{x^2/(1 + x^2)}{1 - 1/(1 + x^2)} \\ &= 1 \qquad (x \neq 0). \end{aligned}$$

Thus

$$\begin{aligned} \lim_{x\to 0} f(x) &= \lim_{x\to 0} \frac{x^2(1 + x^2)}{x^2(1 + x^2)} \\ &= 1. \end{aligned}$$

In short, $f(0)$ and $\lim_{x\to 0} f(x)$ both exist, but have distinct values.

EXERCISES

1. Evaluate the following limits:

   (a) $\lim_{x\to 2} \frac{x^2 - 7x + 1}{x^2 + 9}$, (b) $\lim_{x\to -3} \frac{x^2 - 9}{x^2 + 7x + 12}$,

   (c) $\lim_{h\to 0} \frac{\sqrt{5x + 3h} - \sqrt{5x}}{2h}$, (d) $\lim_{x\to 0} \frac{\sin 3x}{\sin x}$.

2. Make a diagram to justify the inequality

$$\sin x < x < \tan x,$$

   where x is an angle at the centre of a circle of unit radius. Deduce that

$$\lim_{x\to 0} \frac{\sin x}{x} = 1.$$

3. Compute the value $(\sin x)/x$ for $x = 2°, 1°, 15'$.

4. Evaluate the following limits:

   (a) $\lim_{x\to 1} \frac{\sin (x - 1)}{x^3 - 1}$, (b) $\lim_{x\to \pi/2} \frac{\cos x}{x - \frac{1}{2}\pi}$,

   (c) $\lim_{x\to 0} \frac{1 - \cos x}{\sin x}$, (d) $\lim_{x\to \pi/4} \frac{\cos 2x}{\sin x - \cos x}$.

7.5. DIVISION BY ZERO

Before going any further, we must see what value, if any, can be assigned to the two expressions $0/0$ and $a/0$ $(a \neq 0)$. This is easily done.

Suppose $0/0 = x$; by cross-multiplying, we find

$$0 = 0 \cdot x,$$

that is, x is a number which, when multiplied by zero, gives zero. But *any* number has this property; hence the expression $0/0$ is said to be *indeterminate*; it does not suffice to determine any number x.

On the other hand, let us make an attempt to assign some value to the expression $a/0$, with $a \neq 0$; let

$$\frac{a}{0} = y.$$

Then

$$a = 0 \cdot y,$$

that is, y is a number which, when multiplied by zero, gives a. But *no* number has this property; hence the expression $a/0$ is said to be *undefined* or meaningless, since it leads to an impossibility.

We are now in a position to explain the proper use of the symbol ∞; it frequently becomes necessary in mathematics to consider a number's becoming arbitrarily large. The following equivalent statements are made:

n becomes arbitrarily large;
n becomes infinite;
n approaches infinity;
$n \longrightarrow \infty$.

Thus the symbol ∞ is only a useful abbreviation occurring in the context of "becoming infinite" or "approaching infinity".

Example 7.5.1. Evaluate

$$\lim_{n \to \infty} f(n),$$

where

$$f(n) = \frac{1}{n^2 + 1}.$$

Clearly, as n becomes arbitrarily large, then $1/(n^2 + 1)$ approaches zero; we might also say:

$$\text{As} \quad n \longrightarrow \infty, \qquad \frac{1}{n^2 + 1} \longrightarrow 0;$$

or finally,

$$\lim_{n \to \infty} \frac{1}{n^2 + 1} = 0.$$

Thus, the symbol ∞ is used in one manner of speaking.

Example 7.5.2. Evaluate

$$\lim_{n\to\infty} f(n),$$

where

$$f(n) = \frac{n^2 + 3n + 10000}{2n^2 + n + 7}.$$

Clearly, as n becomes arbitrarily large, both

$$n^2 + 3n + 10000 \quad \text{and} \quad 2n^2 + n + 7$$

become arbitrarily large. But what happens to their quotient $f(n)$? We can see the answer by writing $f(n)$ in the equivalent form

$$f(n) = \frac{1 + \dfrac{3}{n} + \dfrac{10000}{n^2}}{2 + \dfrac{1}{n} + \dfrac{7}{n^2}};$$

then, as n becomes arbitrarily large, it is clear that $f(n)$ gets arbitrarily close to $\frac{1}{2}$. Hence, as $n \longrightarrow \infty$, $f(n) \longrightarrow \frac{1}{2}$, that is,

$$\lim_{n\to\infty} f(n) = \tfrac{1}{2}.$$

The use of ∞ as an abbreviation symbol can also occur in other forms; consider

Example 7.5.3. Evaluate

$$\lim_{n\to 3} \left| \frac{n+5}{n^2 - 9} \right|.$$

Here

$$f(n) = \left| \frac{n+5}{n^2 - 9} \right|;$$

it is clear that as n assumes values very close to 3, $f(n)$ becomes *very* large. For instance,

$$f(3.001) = \frac{8.001}{(.001)(6.001)}$$
$$\doteq \frac{8000}{6}.$$

So we may say that "as n gets arbitrarily close to 3, $f(n)$ gets arbitrarily large"; this statement may then be abbreviated to read:

$$\text{As} \quad n \longrightarrow 3, \qquad f(n) \longrightarrow \infty,$$

which may, in turn, be written as

$$\lim_{n\to 3} f(n) = \infty.$$

Example 7.5.4. The student has often encountered the statement that in a geometric series with $|r| < 1$,

$$S_n = a + ar + ar^2 + \cdots + ar^{n-1} = \frac{a(1 - r^n)}{1 - r}.$$

$$S_\infty = \frac{a}{1 - r}.$$

This means that

$$\lim_{n\to\infty} S_n = \frac{a}{1 - r}.$$

In words, "the limit, as n becomes infinite, of S_n, is $a/(1 - r)$". If the student is thinking properly, he should consider this statement as an abbreviation for the longer statement:

"As n becomes arbitrarily large, that is, as we take more and more terms of the geometric series, the sum S_n gets arbitrarily close to the value $a/(1 - r)$".

EXERCISES

1. Evaluate the following limits using the abbreviation sign ∞:

(a) $\displaystyle\lim_{n\to -1} \left|\frac{n^2 + 1}{n + 1}\right|$, (b) $\displaystyle\lim_{m\to 2} \left|\frac{m^2 + 4}{m^2 - 4}\right|$,

(c) $\displaystyle\lim_{x\to\infty} \frac{2x^2 - x}{3x^2 + x}$, (d) $\displaystyle\lim_{x\to\infty} \frac{x^3 + 8}{12x^2 + 9}$,

(e) $\displaystyle\lim_{x\to\infty} \frac{x^2 + x + 10^9}{x^3 + 5}$, (f) $\displaystyle\lim_{y\to\infty} \frac{2^{2y} + 2^{-2y}}{2^{2y} - 2^{-2y}}$,

(g) $\displaystyle\lim_{z\to 0} \frac{2^{2z} - 2^{-2z}}{2^{2z} + 2^{-2z} - 2}$, (h) $\displaystyle\lim_{x\to\infty} \frac{\sin x}{x}$.

2. Explain why the following expressions have no limits:

(a) $\displaystyle\lim_{x\to 5} \frac{1}{(x - 5)^3}$, (b) $\displaystyle\lim_{x\to\infty} \sin x$,

(c) $\displaystyle\lim_{x\to 0} 3^{-1/x}$.

7.6. POSITIVE AND NEGATIVE INFINITY

In the last section, we used the abbreviation $x \longrightarrow \infty$ (or $x \longrightarrow +\infty$) to mean "$x$ assumes arbitrarily large positive values". We shall use the abbreviation $x \longrightarrow -\infty$ to mean "x assumes arbitrarily large negative values".

We shall also use the abbreviations

$$x \longrightarrow a^+ \qquad \text{and} \qquad x \longrightarrow a^-$$

to mean, respectively, "x approaches a through values greater than a", and "x approaches a through values less then a". Thus, $x \longrightarrow 3^+$ will mean that the values x may assume are of the form $3 + \delta$ (δ positive), whereas $x \longrightarrow 3^-$ means that the values x may assume are of the form $3 - \delta$ (δ positive).

Example 7.6.1. Consider

$$\lim_{x\to 3} f(x) \quad \text{where} \quad f(x) = \frac{x+6}{3-x}.$$

Clearly, we may write:

$$\text{As} \quad x \longrightarrow 3^+, \qquad f(x) \longrightarrow -\infty;$$

$$\text{As} \quad x \longrightarrow 3^-, \qquad f(x) \longrightarrow +\infty.$$

Hence, we could write:

$$\lim_{x\to 3^+} f(x) = -\infty, \qquad \lim_{x\to 3^-} f(x) = +\infty.$$

Strictly speaking, we should not refer to

$$\lim_{x\to 3} f(x),$$

although we often say that this limit is infinite [considering only the behaviour of $f(x)$ in magnitude, and not in sign].

Example 7.6.2. $f(x) = 1/(1 - x^2)$; find $f(\frac{1}{2}), f(1)$.
Students at once write

$$f(\tfrac{1}{2}) = \tfrac{4}{3}, \qquad f(1) = \infty.$$

The statement $f(1) = \infty$ is not objectionable *if* the student knows what is meant: "As x gets arbitrarily close to 1, the denominator in $f(x) = 1/(1 - x^2)$ becomes arbitrarily close to zero, that is, the functional value $f(x)$ becomes arbitrarily large numerically".

Actually,

$$\lim_{x\to 1^-} f(x) = +\infty, \qquad \lim_{x\to 1^+} f(x) = -\infty.$$

These two statements are abbreviated forms of the statement: "As x approaches arbitrarily close to 1 through values less (greater) than 1, the functional value $f(x)$ becomes an arbitrarily large positive (negative) number".

Example 7.6.3. Some texts inform the student that $\tan 90° = \pm\infty$. What is this a poor abbreviation for?

The statement really should read:

$$\lim_{x\to 90^{\circ -}} \tan x = +\infty, \qquad \lim_{x\to 90^{\circ +}} \tan x = -\infty;$$

and these two statements are themselves abbreviations for the statements: "As x approaches arbitrarily closely to 90° through values less (greater) than 90°, then $\tan x$ becomes an arbitrarily large positive (negative) number".

Perhaps, in concluding this section, we might summarize some considerations concerning the symbol ∞. Most students have heard that "Infinity is not a number", although they do not really understand the statement. However, there is at least one Ontario secondary school using the formal (and *erroneous*) definition: "Infinity is a very large number with something extra added on"!

Difficulty can be avoided if the student considers that:

(1) infinity is an *abbreviation*;
(2) when infinity is used as an abbreviation, it is used only in a context where a quantity "becomes infinite".

Thus, when we write:

$$\text{as} \quad n \longrightarrow \infty,$$

we read either "as n approaches infinity" or "as n becomes infinite", but we mean these expressions only as *abbreviations* for the statement "as n becomes arbitrarily large", or "as n becomes as large as we please".

Students frequently ask "What is wrong in saying that $f(4) = \infty$ when given $f(x) = 1/|x - 4|$?" Actually, there is no possible objection to writing $f(4) = \infty$ *if* the student realizes that

$$f(4) = \infty$$

is an abbreviation for

$$\text{As} \quad x \longrightarrow 4, \qquad f(x) \longrightarrow \infty,$$

which itself is an abbreviation for "As x gets arbitrarily close to 4, $f(x)$ gets arbitrarily large".

EXERCISES

1. Evaluate the following limits:

(a) $\displaystyle\lim_{x\to 2^+} \frac{x^2 - 4}{x^2 - 5x + 6}$, (b) $\displaystyle\lim_{x\to 2^-} \frac{x^2 - 4}{x^2 - 5x + 6}$,

(c) $\displaystyle\lim_{x\to 2} \frac{x^2 - 4}{x^2 - 5x + 6}$.

2. Evaluate

(a) $\displaystyle\lim_{x\to 2^+} \frac{x + 5}{x^2 - 2x + 4}$, (b) $\displaystyle\lim_{x\to 2^-} \frac{x + 5}{x^2 - 2x + 4}$,

(c) $\displaystyle\lim_{x\to 2} \frac{x + 5}{x^2 - 2x + 4}$.

3. Evaluate

(a) $\lim_{x \to +\infty} \dfrac{x^3 + 9x}{3x^3 - 7x + 4}$, (b) $\lim_{x \to -\infty} \dfrac{x^3 + 9x}{3x^3 - 7x + 4}$,

(c) $\lim_{|x| \to \infty} \dfrac{x^3 + 9x}{3x^3 - 7x + 4}$.

4. Evaluate

(a) $\lim_{x \to 0^+} 2^{1/x}$, (b) $\lim_{x \to 0^-} 2^{-1/x}$.

7.7. SOME INTERESTING LIMITS

In this section, we shall consider some especially complicated limits by means of examples.

Example 7.7.1

$$f(x) = \sin \frac{1}{x}.$$

Evaluate

$$\lim_{x \to 0} f(x).$$

Here, we consider what happens when x is a small fraction of the form

$$\frac{2}{m\pi}, \qquad m \text{ an integer.}$$

Then

$$\begin{aligned} f(x) &= \sin \frac{m\pi}{2} \\ &= 0 \qquad (m \text{ even}) \\ &= \pm 1 \qquad (m \text{ odd}). \end{aligned}$$

So $f(x)$ does not approach any limit but keeps running back and forth from -1 to $+1$; for example, if $x = 2/9999\pi$, then

$$f(x) = \sin \frac{9999\pi}{2} = \sin \frac{3\pi}{2} = -1;$$

if $x = 2/10001\pi$, then

$$f(x) = \sin \frac{10001\pi}{2} = \sin \frac{\pi}{2} = +1.$$

Thus

$$\lim_{x \to 0} f(x)$$

is not defined.

Example 7.7.2. $f(x) = x \sin 1/x$. Here $\lim_{x \to 0} f(x)$ is defined. For, as $x \longrightarrow 0$, $\sin 1/x$ never exceeds 1 in absolute magnitude; and this bounded quantity is multiplied by x, which is getting arbitrarily small. Thus, $x \sin 1/x$ gets arbitrarily small, as $x \longrightarrow 0$; in other words:

$$\text{As} \quad x \longrightarrow 0, \qquad x \sin \frac{1}{x} \longrightarrow 0.$$

Hence

$$\lim_{x \to 0} x \sin \frac{1}{x} = 0.$$

Example 7.7.3. Evaluate

$$\lim_{x \to 0^+} f(x), \qquad \lim_{x \to 0^-} f(x),$$

where

$$f(x) = \frac{1 - 2^{-1/x}}{1 + 2^{-1/x}}.$$

Let $x = 1/n$, where n is a large positive number. Then

$$\lim_{x \to 0^+} f(x) = \lim_{n \to \infty} \frac{1 - 2^{-n}}{1 + 2^{-n}}.$$

As $n \longrightarrow \infty$, 2^n becomes arbitrarily large, and hence 2^{-n} approaches zero. Hence,

$$\lim_{n \to \infty} \frac{1 - 2^{-n}}{1 + 2^{-n}} = 1.$$

On the other hand, if $x = -1/n$, where n is a large positive number, we have

$$\begin{aligned} \lim_{x \to 0^-} f(x) &= \lim_{n \to \infty} \frac{1 - 2^n}{1 + 2^n} \\ &= \lim_{n \to \infty} \frac{2^{-n} - 1}{2^{-n} + 1} \\ &= -1, \end{aligned}$$

using the same argument as before.

EXERCISES

1. Evaluate

$$\lim_{x \to 0^+} f(x), \qquad \lim_{x \to 0^-} f(x),$$

where

$$f(x) = \frac{1 - 2^{-1/x}}{1 + 2^{+1/x}}.$$

2. Evaluate

$$\lim_{x \to \infty} \sin \frac{1}{x}.$$

7.8. GRAPHS OF FUNCTIONS

The graph of a function $y = f(x)$ comprises all those points and only those points (x_i, y_i) in a Cartesian coordinate system which have the property that $y_i = f(x_i)$.

For example, let $y = x^2$. It is clear that the point (2, 7) is not part of the graph of this function, since $7 > 2^2$; also, (2, 3) is not part of the graph of the function, since $3 < 2^2$. On the other hand, (2, 4) is part of the graph of the function, since $4 = 2^2$.

Obviously, it would be ridiculous (and impossible) to test every point (x, y) in the Cartesian plane to see whether or not it lies on the graph of a given function $y = f(x)$. What we do is find a few points on the graph and then employ the *continuity* property of most functions. Before discussing continuity, let us look at an example.

Example 7.8.1. Graph the function

$$f(x) = x^2 - 3x + 1.$$

It is easy to find a few values and tabulate them as follows.

x:	-3	-2	-1	0	1	2	3	4
$f(x)$:	19	11	5	1	-1	-1	1	5

These pairs of corresponding values $[x, f(x)]$ can be plotted as points in the Cartesian plane, and joined by a smooth continuous curve (Figure 7.1). When we do this, we are assuming that $f(3.5)$ lies in a reasonable position between $f(3)$ and $f(4)$, that is, that there are no abrupt breaks in the curve.

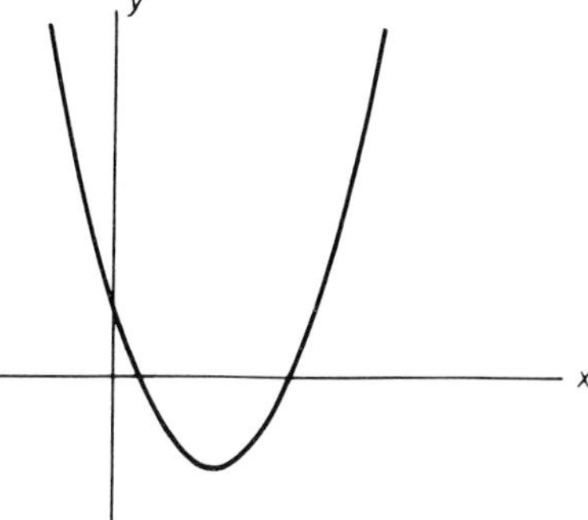

Figure 7.1

Some curves differ from the curve in Figure 7.1 in that they do possess breaks. We now make the

DEFINITION. A single-valued function is *continuous* at the place $x = a$ if

$$\lim_{x\to a^+} f(x) = \lim_{x\to a^-} f(x) = f(a).$$

In other words, such a function is continuous at $x = a$ if $f(a)$ exists and if the functional values to the right and left of $f(a)$ approach $f(a)$. This is the normal situation.

If a function is continuous for all values of x, we say the function is a continuous function. The function in Example 7.8.1 is a continuous function.

Example 7.8.2.

$$f(x) = (x - 2)^{-1}.$$

Here it is clear that

$$\lim_{x\to 2^+} f(x) = +\infty,$$
$$\lim_{x\to 2^-} f(x) = -\infty,$$
$$f(2) \text{ is undefined.}$$

This situation is illustrated in Figure 7.2; the graph of $f(x)$ is continuous without any breaks except at $x = 2$ (quite a break there!). This type of infinite discontinuity is the commonest discontinuity met in elementary work.

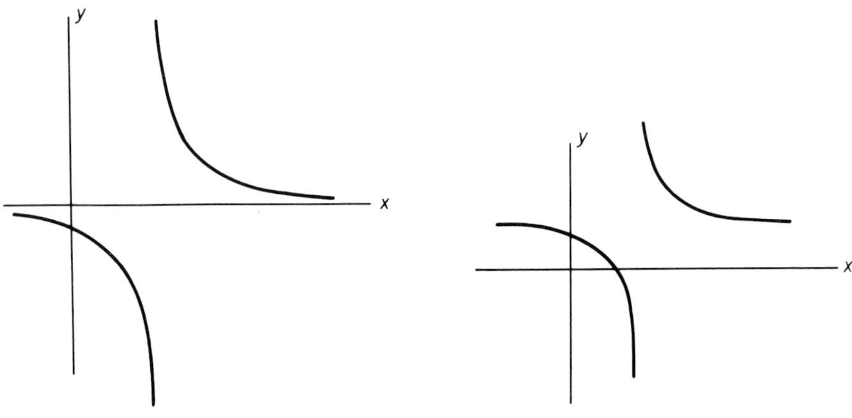

Figure 7.2

Figure 7.3

Sometimes, evaluation of certain limits is very helpful in drawing graphs. Let us consider

Example 7.8.3. Graph $f(x) = (2x - 4)/(x - 3)$.

It is clear that

$$\lim_{|x|\to\infty} f(x) = \lim_{|x|\to\infty} \frac{2 - 4/x}{1 - 3/x} = 2.$$

Hence, as $|x| \longrightarrow \infty$, $f(x) \longrightarrow 2$; in other words, as x becomes arbitrarily large either positively or negatively, $f(x)$ gets arbitrarily close to 2.

It is clear also that

$$\lim_{x\to 3^+} f(x) = +\infty, \qquad \lim_{x\to 3^-} f(x) = -\infty.$$

In short, there is an infinite discontinuity at $x = 3$. These facts, together with a few selected values such as $f(2) = 0$, allow us to make the graph shown in Figure 7.3.

It might not be inappropriate here to make a distinction between *plotting* a curve and *sketching* a curve. In Example 7.8.1, we *plotted* the curve (Figure 7.1) by ascertaining a considerable number of points on the graph, and then carefully drawing a curve through them. In Example 7.8.3 (cf. Figure 7.3), we found out the general features of the curve, and these enable us to *sketch* the general form of the graph without finding a single specific point. Sketching graphs is of great importance, since the general shape of the graph, rather than a slavish adherence to exact position, is usually most significant.

As an illustration of a more complicated discontinuity, consider

Example 7.8.4

$$f(x) = x^2 + \frac{x^2}{1 + x^2} + \frac{x^2}{(1 + x^2)^2} + \frac{x^2}{(1 + x^2)^3} + \cdots$$

Let us compare $f(0)$ and $\lim_{x \to 0} f(x)$.

Here $f(0) = 0$. For $x \neq 0$, we have a convergent infinite geometric series; so

$$f(x) = \frac{x^2}{1 - \dfrac{1}{1 + x^2}} = 1 + x^2.$$

Hence,

$$\lim_{x \to 0} f(x) = \lim_{x \to 0} (1 + x^2) = 1.$$

Thus, when $x = 0$, the functional value is zero; but as $x \longrightarrow 0$ the functional value approaches 1.

This situation is best described by looking at the graph; the point (0, 1) is *not* on the graph of $f(x)$ (cf. Figure 7.4). Here there is a finite discontinuity for $x = 0$;

$$f(0) \neq \lim_{x \to 0} f(x).$$

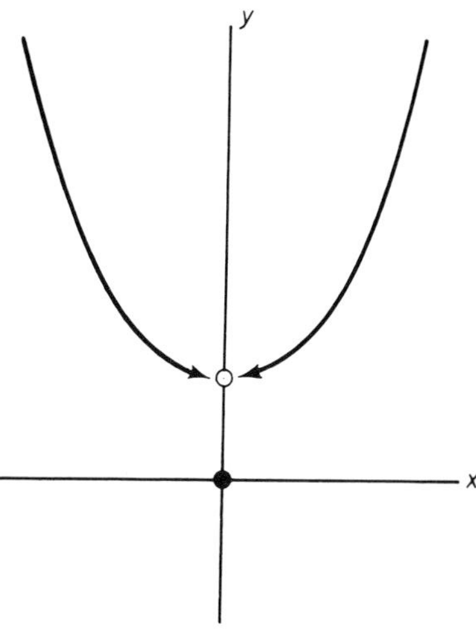

Figure 7.4

Probably the worst thing that can happen occurs for the function of Example 7.7.3. We consider it again in

Example 7.8.5

$$f(x) = \frac{1 - 2^{-1/x}}{1 + 2^{-1/x}}.$$

Here $f(0)$ is undefined, but we found

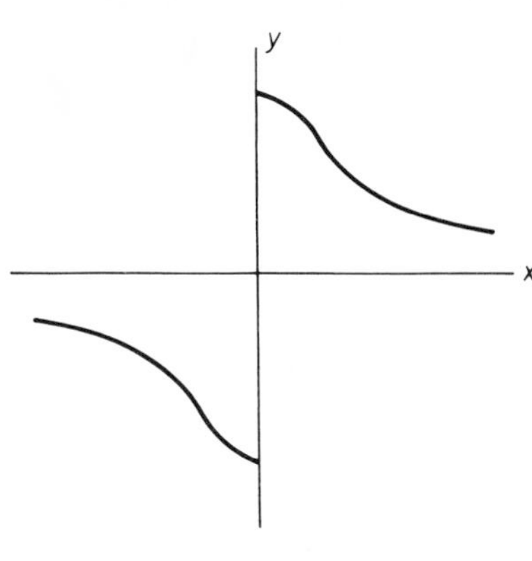

Figure 7.5

$$\lim_{x\to 0^+} f(x) = +1, \qquad \lim_{x\to 0^-} f(x) = -1.$$

It is also clear that

$$\lim_{|x|\to\infty} f(x) = 0,$$

since

$$2^{-1/x} \longrightarrow 1 \quad \text{as} \quad |x| \longrightarrow \infty.$$

This situation is illustrated in Figure 7.5.

Example 7.8.6. We might note that the functions

$$y = \sin\frac{1}{x} \quad \text{and} \quad y = x\sin\frac{1}{x}$$

of Examples 7.7.1 and 7.7.2 have rather interesting graphs as regards continuity; they are shown in Figures 7.6 and 7.7 respectively (there is an infinite number of loops in $0 \leq x \leq 1$).

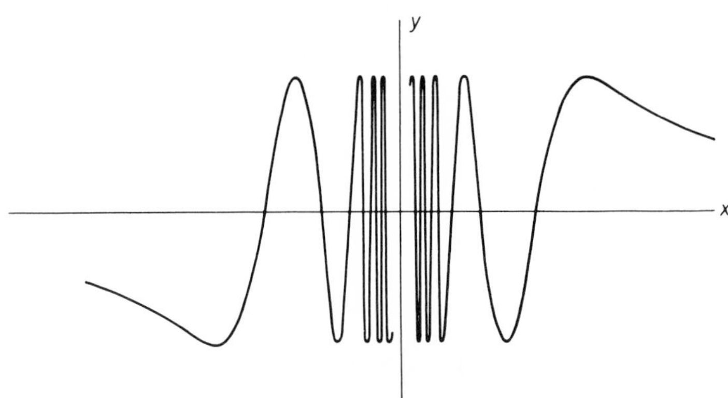

Figure 7.6

It is instructive to sketch a few graphs of positive functions.

Example 7.8.7. Sketch the graph of

$$y = |x^2 - 5x + 6|.$$

Clearly $y \geq 0$; also, $y = 0$ only for $x = 2$ or $x = 3$. The graph consists of portions of two parabolas, as shown in Figure 7.8.

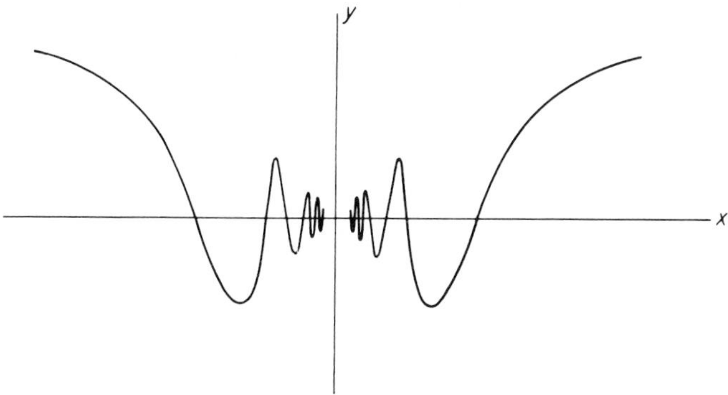

Figure 7.7

Example 7.8.8. Sketch the graph of

$$y = \left| \frac{3(x-2)(x-4)}{(x+2)(x-7)} \right| .$$

Again $y \geq 0$; $y = 0$ if $x = 2$ or $x = 4$. Furthermore,

$$\lim_{x\to -2} y = +\infty, \quad \lim_{x\to 7} y = +\infty, \quad \lim_{|x|\to\infty} y = 3.$$

These facts allow us to make the sketch in Figure 7.9.

Finally, we note that a sketch can often be made if we merely note when a function is positive or negative.

Example 7.8.9. Sketch the graph of

$$y = x(x-1)(x-3)(x+1)(x+4).$$

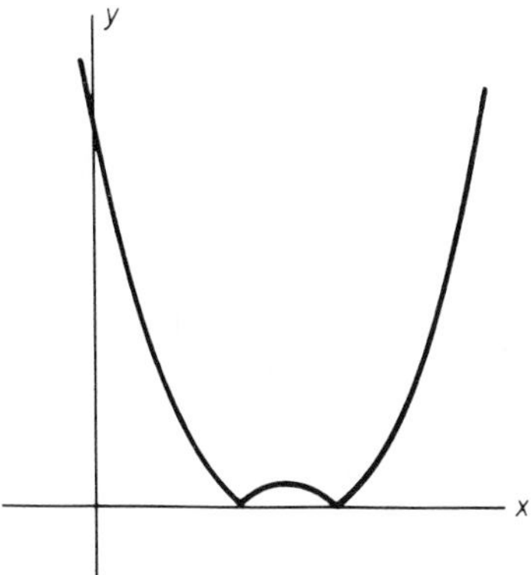

Figure 7.8

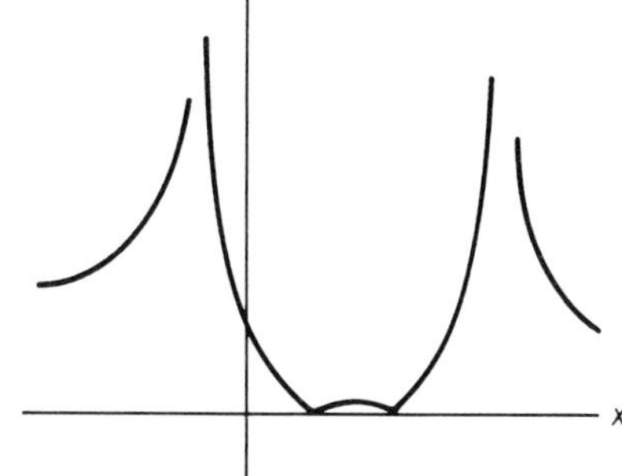

Figure 7.9

We see that y vanishes for $x = 0, 1, 3, -1, -4$. Also, for x between 0 and 1, the factors x, $x + 1$, $x + 4$, are positive whereas the factors $x - 1$, $x - 3$, are negative; hence y is positive. Similar considerations produce the results:

$$\begin{aligned} 0 < x < \ \ 1&: \ y \text{ positive;} \\ 1 < x < \ \ 3&: \ y \text{ negative;} \\ x > \ \ 3&: \ y \text{ positive;} \\ -1 < x < \ \ 0&: \ y \text{ negative;} \\ -4 < x < -1&: \ y \text{ positive;} \\ x < -4&: \ y \text{ negative.} \end{aligned}$$

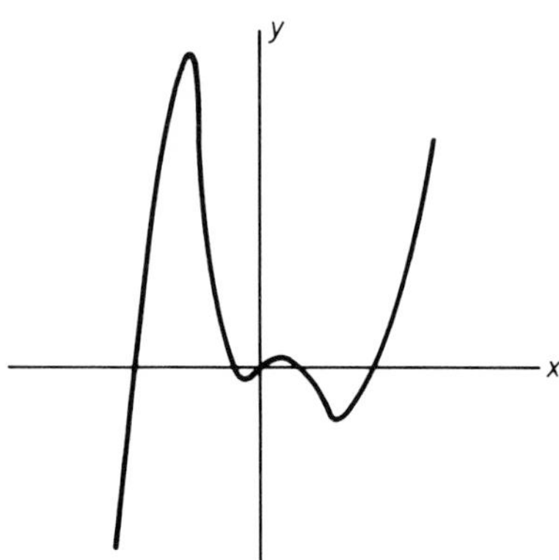

Figure 7.10

It is also obvious that

$$\lim_{x \to \infty} y = \infty, \qquad \lim_{x \to -\infty} y = -\infty.$$

The resulting graph is shown in Figure 7.10.

EXERCISES

1. Locate the points of discontinuity of the following functions:

(a) $f(x) = \dfrac{1}{x^2}$, (b) $f(x) = \dfrac{x^2 - 9}{x^2 - 8x + 15}$,

(c) $f(x) = \dfrac{3x - 3}{2x + 5}$, (d) $f(x) = 3^{-1/x^2}$.

In each case, graph the function.

2. Distinguish between the graphs of the following functions:

(a) $y = x + 3$, (b) $y = \dfrac{x^2 - 9}{x - 3}$.

(c) $y(x - 3) = x^2 - 9$.

3. Graph the following functions:

(a) $[f(x)]^2 = x(x - 3)^2$, (b) $f(x) = x \log_{10} x$,

(c) $f(x) = \dfrac{x^2 - 4}{x(x + 5)}$, (d) $f(x) = \dfrac{x(x - 1)(x - 2)}{(x + 1)(x + 2)(x + 3)}$.

4. Given $f(x) = x^{-2}$, show that $f(x)$ is continuous for $x = 3$ by finding δ such that, given $0 < \epsilon < \frac{1}{10}$,

$$|f(x) - \tfrac{1}{9}| < \epsilon,$$

whenever $|x - 3| < \delta$.

5. Plot the graph of

$$f(x) = \frac{x}{2^x}.$$

6. Let $\sqrt{u}$ be the distance from the point $(-1, 0)$ to the point (X, Y) on the parabola $y^2 = 4x$. Show that

$$u = X^2 + 6X + 1,$$

and sketch the graph of u as a function of X (note that u is defined only for $X \geq 0$).

7. A wire of length 10 units is cut into two parts of lengths x and $10 - x$; these parts are bent to form a circle and a square respectively. Show that, if A is the total area of circle and square, then (taking $\pi = \frac{22}{7}$)

$$A = \tfrac{5}{176}[5x^2 - 44x + 220].$$

Sketch the graph of A as a function of x (note that physical considerations restrict x to the range $0 \leq x \leq 10$).

8. Graph the functions

(a) $y = x^3 - 3x$, (b) $v = u^3 - 3u$,

(c) $w = z^3 - 3z$.

9. Sketch graphs for the functions given by

(a) $y = \dfrac{|x|}{x}$, (b) $y = \left|\dfrac{x - 1}{x + 2}\right|$,

(c) $y = |x^3 - 4x|$, (d) $y = |x|$,

(e) $y = |\sin x|$, (f) $y = x + |x|$,

(g) $y = (x^2 - 9) - |x^2 - 9|$.

10. What is the relation between the graphs of the following functions?

(a) $y = (x^2 - 1)(x^2 - 4)$. (b) $y = |x^2 - 1|\,|x^2 - 4|$.

(c) $y = (x^2 - 1)\,|x^2 - 4|$. (d) $y = |x^2 - 1|\,(x^2 - 4)$.

7.9. EXPLICIT, IMPLICIT, AND PARAMETRIC DEFINITIONS

Common functions are usually defined in one of three ways, which will now be described.

Suppose that y is defined directly by a relation such as

$$y = x^2 - 2x + 5.$$

Then we say that y is defined *explicitly* in terms of x. This is a very common situation, and y is normally a single-valued function of x.

However, it may be that y is related indirectly to x; for example, if

$$3x + 4y - 8 = 0.$$

Then we say that y is defined *implicitly* as a function of x; in this particular illustration, it is easy to give y explicitly as a function of x, namely,

$$y = \frac{8 - 3x}{4}.$$

However, complications frequently arise when y is given implicitly in terms of x; usually, in such a case, several values of y correspond to any particular value of x. Let us consider

Example 7.9.1

$$x^2 + y^2 = 25.$$

The graph obtained here is a circle, but, if we attempt to solve for y in terms of x, we get

$$y = \pm\sqrt{25 - x^2}$$

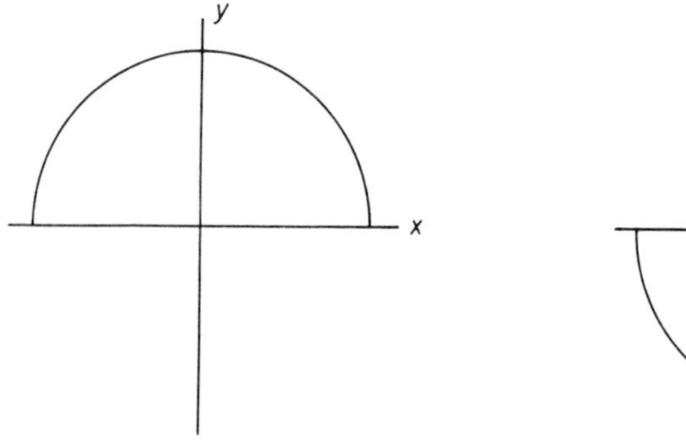

Figure 7.11

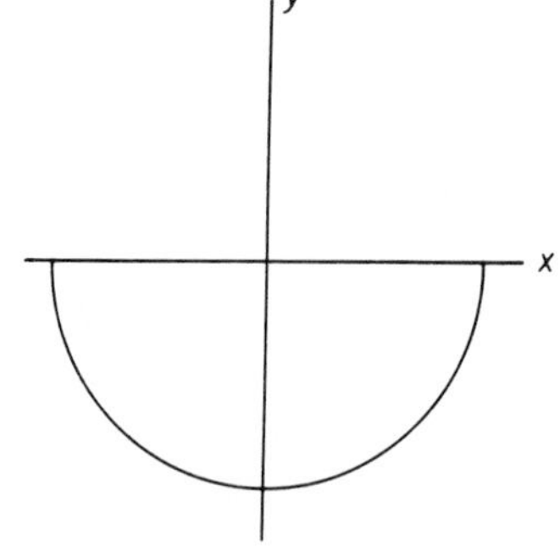

Figure 7.12

(since, for any x, we may take y either $+$ or $-$). There are exactly two *continuous* single-valued functions, namely,

$$y = +\sqrt{25 - x^2},$$

illustrated in Figure 7.11, and

$$y = -\sqrt{25 - x^2},$$

illustrated in Figure 7.12. Two of the many possible single-valued discontinuous functions which satisfy the relation

$$x^2 + y^2 = 25$$

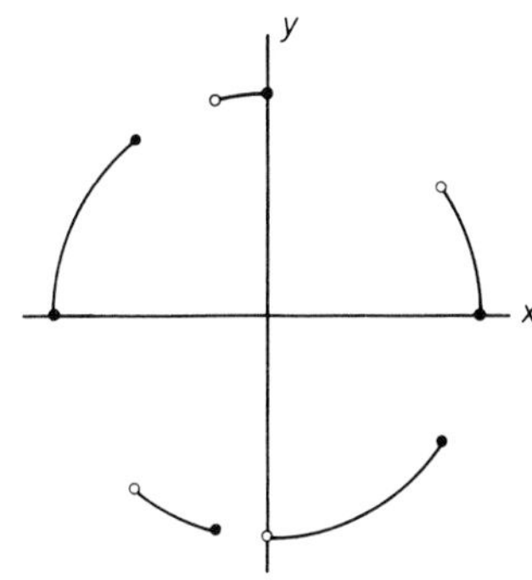

Figure 7.13

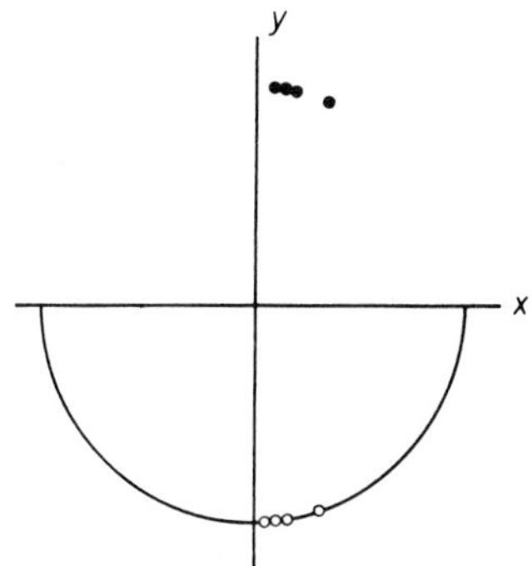

Figure 7.14

are shown in Figures 7.13 and 7.14. Figure 7.13 illustrates the function

$$\begin{aligned}
y &= +\sqrt{25 - x^2} && \text{in } -5 \le x \le -3,\\
y &= -\sqrt{25 - x^2} && \text{in } -3 < x \le -1,\\
y &= +\sqrt{25 - x^2} && \text{in } -1 < x \le 0,\\
y &= -\sqrt{25 - x^2} && \text{in } \quad 0 < x \le 4,\\
y &= +\sqrt{25 - x^2} && \text{in } \quad 4 < x \le 5.
\end{aligned}$$

Figure 7.14 illustrates a function with an infinite set of discontinuities, namely,

$$\begin{aligned}
f(x) &= +\sqrt{25 - x^2} && \text{for } x = 1/n \quad (n \text{ a positive integer}),\\
f(x) &= -\sqrt{25 - x^2} && \text{otherwise.}
\end{aligned}$$

Finally, a function may be defined parametrically, that is, x and y may both be given in terms of a third quantity, the *parameter*, which acts as a connecting link or liaison between x and y. Consider

Example 7.9.2

$$x = 3 \sin t,\ y = 2 \operatorname{cosec} t.$$

It is clear that

$$xy = 6,$$

that is, the parameter may, in *this particular case*, easily be eliminated.

It should be noted that the parametric form of a functional relation is the most general form in that the function represented by $y = f(x)$ can always be represented parametrically by

$$x = t,\ y = f(t).$$

In examples more complicated than Example 7.9.2, eliminating the parameter may make work more difficult.

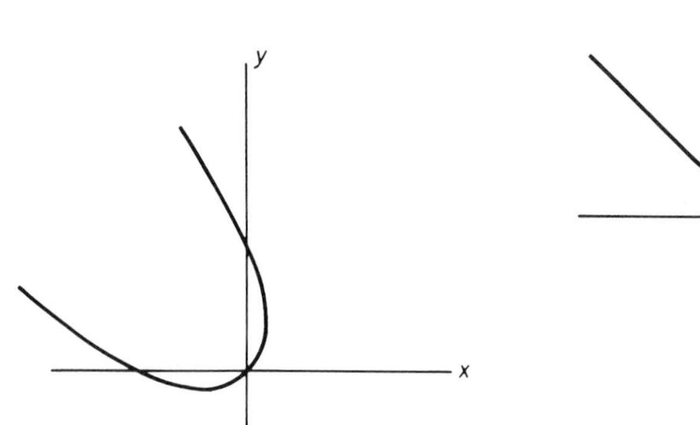

Figure 7.15

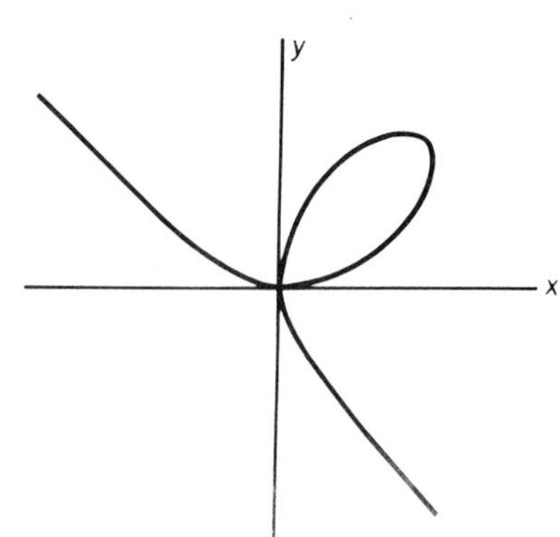

Figure 7.16

Example 7.9.3. Find the Cartesian equation for the graph given by

$$x = t - t^2, \qquad y = t + t^2.$$

Here we find $x + y = 2t$. Hence,

$$y = \tfrac{1}{2}(x + y) + \tfrac{1}{4}(x + y)^2.$$

Simplifying,

$$4y = 2x + 2y + x^2 + 2xy + y^2,$$

that is,

$$x^2 + 2xy + y^2 + 2x - 2y = 0.$$

Obviously, this implicit form of the functional relation is not as simple as the given parametric form. And, if we use the quadratic formula to solve for y in terms of x, we obtain

$$y = (1 - x) \pm \sqrt{1 - 4x},$$

which involves a surd. The simplest way to graph the given function is to assign values to t in the relation

$$x = t - t^2, \qquad y = t + t^2.$$

For example, $t = 2$ gives the point $(-2, 6)$. Having obtained a few points, we may complete the (parabolic) graph, as in Figure 7.15.

Sometimes it even pays to convert a Cartesian equation into parametric form. This procedure is illustrated in

Example 7.9.4. Graph the curve

$$x^3 + y^3 - xy = 0.$$

We note that the curve passes through the origin (0, 0); so we find where the line $y = mx$ cuts the curve. Solving $y = mx$ with the equation of the curve, the point of intersection is

$$\left(\frac{m}{1 + m^3}, \frac{m^2}{1 + m^3}\right).$$

In other words,

$$x = \frac{m}{1 + m^3}, \quad y = \frac{m^2}{1 + m^3}$$

is a parametric representation for an arbitrary point upon the curve. By assigning values to m, we obtain enough points to plot the curve; this is done in Figure 7.16.

EXERCISES

1. Express y implicitly as a function of x, given

$$y = x^2 - 3x + 7.$$

2. Express y explicitly as a function of x, given

(a) $5x + 7y = 2$, (b) $x^2 - 2y^2 = 8$,

(c) $\dfrac{x^2}{9} + \dfrac{y^2}{4} = 1$.

3. Express y implicitly as a function of x, given

(a) $x = \cos\theta$, $y = \sin\theta$; (b) $x = \sec\theta$, $y = \tan\theta$;

(c) $x = 3t$, $y = 2t^2 - 1$; (d) $x = \sin t$, $y = \cos 2t$;

(e) $x = t + 4$, $y = 3t - 7$.

8

Fundamental Concepts of Calculus

by Douglas G. Wertheim

8.1. INTRODUCTION

The discussion in this chapter is an attempt to present some of the basic concepts of calculus in such a way that the structure of the subject may be seen; there has been no attempt to achieve either completeness of presentation or hair-splitting accuracy of definition and argument.

The study of calculus may be described as the study of what results when one new operation, the operation known as "taking a limit", is added to the standard operations of addition, subtraction, multiplication, and division, and all five operations are applied to functions.

The genesis of calculus was the desire to give precise meaning to certain phrases such as "velocity at a point", "tangent to a curve", "area under a curve", "area enclosed by curved lines", etc. Some of these problems were of considerable antiquity; the Greeks, for example, recognized the difficulty involved in speaking of *velocity* (a concept requiring the ideas of extension in time and space) *at a point.* When each of these problems was resolved, it was found that, at the core of the problem, lay the concept of limit. We

Table 8.1. CONCEPTS OF CHAPTER 8

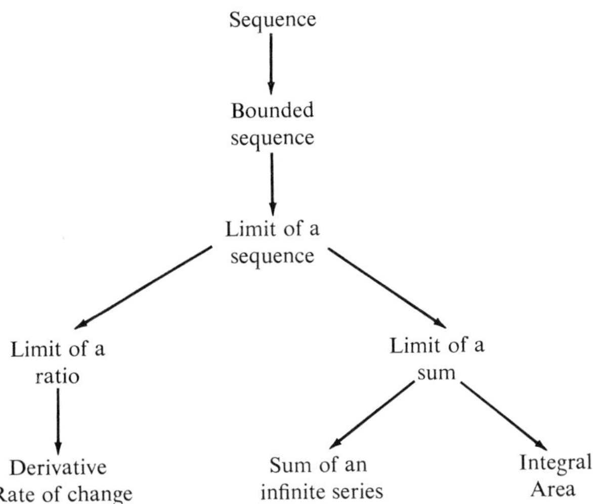

shall take this concept as our starting point, and work onward from it; a block diagram of the discussion is given in Table 8.1.

8.2. SEQUENCES

We begin with an explanation of some of the common terms in use.

DEFINITION. A *sequence* is a set of elements that may be put into one-to-one correspondence with the natural numbers 1, 2, 3, . . . or some subset thereof. Sequences may consist of only a finite number of terms, but such sequences are of relatively little interest; when the term *sequence* is used in this chapter, it will be understood to mean an infinite sequence. The sequence of terms $u_1, u_2, u_3, \ldots$ is designated by the standard notation $\{u_n\}$, $n = 1, 2, 3, \ldots.$

Example 8.2.1. The set of real numbers

$$\pi, \quad \pi^2, \quad \pi^3, \quad 1, \quad 2, \quad 3,$$

is a finite sequence $\{u_n\}$, $n = 1, 2, 3, 4, 5, 6$, with

$$u_1 = \pi, \quad u_2 = \pi^2, \quad u_3 = \pi^3, \quad u_4 = 1, \quad u_5 = 2, \quad u_6 = 3.$$

Example 8.2.2. The sequence $\{u_n\}$, $n = 1, 2, 3, \ldots$ defined by the law $u_n = n^2 - n$ is an infinite sequence. The first few terms are

$$u_1 = 0, \quad u_2 = 2, \quad u_3 = 6, \quad u_4 = 12, \quad u_5 = 20, \quad \ldots.$$

DEFINITION. *A bounded sequence of numbers* is a sequence of numbers $u_1, u_2, u_3, \ldots$ such that all the u's are less than or at most equal to some number M and greater than or at least equal to some number m. We use the notation

$$\{u_n\}, \quad n = 1, 2, \ldots; \qquad m \leq u_n \leq M, \quad n = 1, 2, 3, \ldots.$$

Example 8.2.3. The sequence defined by

$$a_n = 1 + \frac{1}{n} \qquad (n = 1, 2, 3, \ldots)$$

is a bounded sequence. For a_n is equal to unity increased by a positive number; so $a_n > 1$. Also, this positive number $1/n$ cannot exceed 1; hence $a_n \leq 2$. Thus we may write

$$1 < a_n \leq 2; \qquad n = 1, 2, 3, \ldots.$$

The first few terms of the sequence are

$$a_1 = 2, \quad a_2 = \tfrac{3}{2}, \quad a_3 = \tfrac{4}{3}, \quad a_4 = \tfrac{5}{4}, \quad \ldots.$$

Example 8.2.4. The sequence defined by

$$b_n = 2 \sin \frac{\pi}{n} \qquad (n = 1, 2, 3, \ldots)$$

is bounded. For the sine function can never exceed 1 in absolute value, no matter what value n assumes. Consequently,

$$-2 \leq b_n \leq 2 \qquad (n = 1, 2, 3, \ldots).$$

Example 8.2.5. The sequence defined by

$$u_n = 2n + 3 \qquad (n = 1, 2, 3, \ldots)$$

is not bounded. Although $u_n \geq 5$ for all n, we see that u_n can be made arbitrarily large as n gets arbitrarily large. Thus, there is no upper bound M for this sequence.

In general, the number M referred to in the definition of a bounded sequence is called an *upper bound* for the sequence; similarly, m is called a *lower bound.* These numbers M and m are not unique.

Example 8.2.6. In Example 8.2.3, we found that

$$1 < a_n \leq 2 \qquad (n = 1, 2, 3, \ldots);$$

so 1 is a lower bound, and 2 is an upper bound. But obviously we could also write

$$-\tfrac{1}{2} < a_n \leq \pi;$$

so $-\frac{1}{2}$ is also a lower bound, and π is an upper bound. However, 1 is the *greatest lower bound* for the sequence, since all other lower bounds are less than 1. Similarly, 2 is the *least upper bound* for $\{a_n\}$; all other upper bounds exceed 2.

The greatest lower bound and the least upper bound of a sequence may or may not be members of the sequence; in this example, the least upper bound is a member (for $n = 1$), but the greatest lower bound is not (no value of n makes $a_n = 1$).

Example 8.2.7. The sequence of Example 8.2.4 has 0 as greatest lower bound, $+2$ as least upper bound; both happen to be members of the sequence, since $a_1 = 0$, $a_2 = 2$; all other terms lie between 0 and 2, since

$$a_n = 2(\text{sine of an acute angle})$$

for $n > 2$.

Definition. Given a sequence of numbers $\{u_n\}$, $n = 1, 2, 3, \ldots$, a number A is said to be the *limit of the sequence of numbers* if, for every interval $(A - \epsilon, A + \epsilon)$, with $\epsilon > 0$, all but a finite number of the u's are found in the interval. We may also state this result in another way: If, for *every* $\epsilon > 0$ that is given to us, we can produce an integer N (which will depend on ϵ) such that $A - \epsilon < u_n < A + \epsilon$ for $n = N + 1, N + 2, \ldots$, then A is said to be the limit of the sequence.

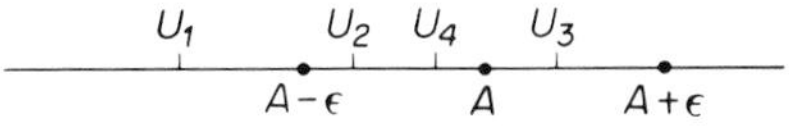

Figure 8.1

Remarks:

(1) ϵ is *any* positive, non-zero number; it is used merely to specify the length of the interval about A (cf. Figure 8.1).
(2) A is sometimes a member of the sequence that defines it, and sometimes it is not. Whether it belongs or fails to belong to the sequence is generally of little interest.
(3) The essence of the idea of limit is this: From a certain stage onward, *all* the members of the sequence cluster arbitrarily closely about the limit A (within a distance ϵ of A, ϵ arbitrary); in short, all the terms of the sequence from u_N onward lie within a distance ϵ of A.
(4) The non-existence of the limit of a sequence is the rule rather than the exception.
(5) A sequence may have infinitely many of its members clustering around one point P_1, and infinitely many others clustering about some other point P_2. Such points are called *points of accumulation.*

The concept of limit of a sequence can best be understood by illustrative examples; we shall give a selection which also illustrates the remarks made concerning limits.

Example 8.2.8

$$\{u_n\} = \frac{(-1)^{n+1}}{n}, \qquad n = 1, 2, 3, \ldots.$$

Here, 0 is the limit of the sequence $1, -\frac{1}{2}, \frac{1}{3}, -\frac{1}{4}, \ldots$. Note that 0 does not belong to the sequence, that is, for no value of n does $u_n = 0$.

However, for any ϵ, all terms past a certain stage lie in the range $-\epsilon \leq u_n \leq \epsilon$. Suppose we take $\epsilon = .006$; then it is easy to find that $N = 167$. For $n \geq N$, we have

$$|u_n - 0| \leq |u_N - 0| = 1/167 = .00598\ldots.$$

Consequently, all terms in the sequence, from the 167th term onward, lie within .006 units of the limit 0. Had we selected a smaller ϵ, the corresponding N would have been greater.

Example 8.2.9

$$u_{2n} = \frac{1}{n}; \quad u_{2n-1} = 1 - \frac{1}{n}; \qquad n = 1, 2, 3, \ldots.$$

Computing the first few terms, we find that

$$u_1 = 0, \quad u_2 = 1, \quad u_3 = \tfrac{1}{2}, \quad u_4 = \tfrac{1}{2}, \quad u_5 = \tfrac{2}{3}, \quad u_6 = \tfrac{1}{3}.$$

This sequence has two points of accumulation (0 and 1) and no limit (since the sequence never settles down to clustering about just one point).

The even-numbered terms u_{2n} get arbitrarily close to 0 for n very large, whereas the odd-numbered terms u_{2n-1} get arbitrarily close to 1 for n very large. For example, $u_{99} = .98$, $u_{100} = .02$.

Example 8.2.10

$$u_n = \frac{1}{2n}, \quad n = 1, 2, \ldots, 50; \qquad u_n = 1, \quad n > 50.$$

This sequence is

$$\tfrac{1}{2}, \tfrac{1}{4}, \tfrac{1}{6}, \tfrac{1}{8}, \ldots, \tfrac{1}{98}, \tfrac{1}{100}, 1, 1, \ldots, 1, \ldots.$$

We note that the sequence is bounded below by 0 and above by 2 (or we might use .0005 and 1.537 as lower and upper bounds). We note also that 1 is the limit of the sequence, and 1 is actually a number of the sequence.

Example 8.2.11

$$u_n = 3^n \qquad (n = 1, 2, \ldots).$$

This sequence 3, 9, 27, 81, 243, ... is not a bounded sequence; it is bounded below by 1.34, but is unbounded above. It has no limit. (Of course, 3 is the greatest lower bound.)

Example 8.2.12. Find the next term in the sequence 1, 3, 5, 7, ...

This is a sort of question which is very popular on psychological tests; unless further information (such as the sequence's being an arithmetic progression) is given, there is no answer. One might argue that the next term is 9 (assuming the sequence to be an arithmetic progression) or that the next term is 11 (assuming the sequence to be the sequence of 1 and the odd prime numbers). On the other hand, the formula

$$u_n = 2n - 1 + (n - 1)(n - 2)(n - 3)(n - 4)f(n),$$

where $f(n)$ is an arbitrary function of n, supplies an infinitude of answers. If we wanted the fifth term u_5 to be 97, we could take as the general term

$$u_n = 2n - 1 + \tfrac{88}{24}(n - 1)(n - 2)(n - 3)(n - 4).$$

8.3. PROPERTIES OF SEQUENCES

In this section, we shall recall some fundamental theorems on the existence of limits for sequences.

THEOREM 8.3.1. If a sequence of numbers $\{u_n\}$ is monotonely increasing (that is, $u_1 \leq u_2 \leq u_3 \leq \cdots$) and bounded above by some number M, then the sequence approaches a limit A where $A \leq M$.

Example 8.3.1

$$u_n = 2 - \frac{1}{2^{n-1}}; \quad n = 1, 2, 3, \ldots.$$

Here $M = 2$, $A = 2$. The terms of the sequence are all less than 2, but approach arbitrarily close to 2 as n gets larger. The situation is illustrated graphically in Figure 8.2.

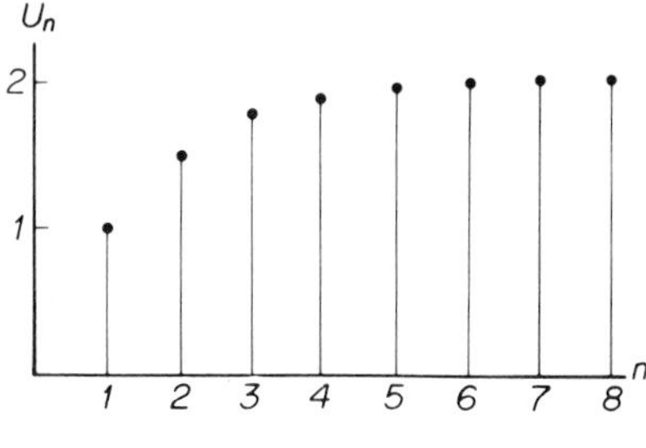

Figure 8.2

THEOREM 8.3.2. If a sequence is monotonely decreasing (that is, $u_1 \geq u_2 \geq u_3 \geq \cdots$) and bounded below by a number m, then it approaches a limit B where $m \leq B$.

Example 8.3.2. Show that the sequence

$$a_n = \frac{n^2 + 1}{n^2} \qquad (n = 1, 2, 3, \ldots)$$

approaches a limit.

Here

$$a_n = 1 + \frac{1}{n^2}.$$

So the sequence is monotonely decreasing and bounded below by 1; thus (Theorem 8.3.2) it approaches a limit (actually the limit is 1, since we see that a_n can be made arbitrarily close to 1 for n sufficiently large). This situation is shown in Figure 8.3.

THEOREM 8.3.3. The necessary and sufficient condition that a sequence $\{u_n\}$ be *convergent* (that is, approach a limit) is that, for any given $\epsilon > 0$, it is possible to produce an N (N depending on ϵ) such that

$$|u_m - u_n| < \epsilon \qquad \text{for all } m > n > N.$$

Theorem 8.3.3 is known as the *Cauchy Criterion.*

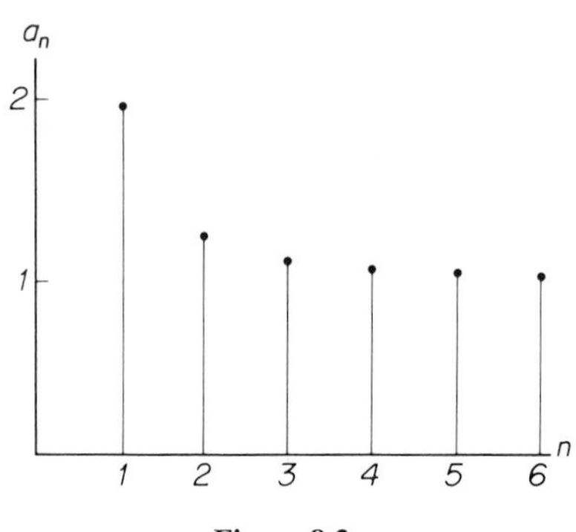

Figure 8.3

Example 8.3.3. Find an N (cf. Theorem 8.3.3) for the sequence $\{u_n\}$, where

$$u_n = \sin \frac{\pi}{n} \qquad (n = 1, 2, 3, \ldots).$$

We wish to have $|u_m - u_n| < \epsilon$; hence

$$\left| \sin \frac{\pi}{m} - \sin \frac{\pi}{n} \right| < \epsilon,$$

$$2\left| \cos \left(\frac{\pi}{2m} + \frac{\pi}{2n}\right)\right|\left| \sin \left(\frac{\pi}{2m} - \frac{\pi}{2n}\right)\right| < \epsilon.$$

This condition is certainly true if we demand that

$$2 \sin \left(\frac{\pi}{2m} - \frac{\pi}{2n}\right) < \epsilon.$$

This condition certainly holds if

$$2 \sin \frac{\pi}{2m} < \epsilon$$

(assuming that m is the smaller of m and n). Since $\sin y < y$ for all $y > 0$, we can satisfy the condition by taking

$$\frac{2\pi}{2m} < \epsilon.$$

Hence, $\pi < \epsilon m$, $m > \pi/\epsilon$. Thus, if we take N to be an integer greater than π/ϵ, we know that

$$|u_m - u_n| < \epsilon \qquad \text{for } m, n > N.$$

Example 8.3.4. Consider the sequence of positive terms:

$$a_1 = 2, \quad a_n = \sqrt{3 + a_{n-1}} \qquad (n \geq 1).$$

This sequence can best be discussed under three headings.

(a) *Boundedness.* We are given $a_1 = 2$; thus, $a_1 < 4$. Also, if we assume $a_{n-1} < 4$, we see that $a_n < \sqrt{3 + 4} < 4$. Thus, using mathematical induction (Chapter 4), we see that *the sequence is bounded above by 4.*

(b) *Monotony.* Clearly

$$a_2 - a_1 = \sqrt{5} - 2 > 0.$$

Also

$$a_{n+1}^2 - a_n^2 = (3 + a_n) - (3 + a_{n-1}) = a_n - a_{n-1}.$$

Consequently, if we assume that $a_n - a_{n-1} > 0$, it follows that $a_{n+1}^2 - a_n^2 > 0$, that is,

$$a_{n+1}^2 > a_n^2, \qquad a_{n+1} > a_n.$$

Again, mathematical induction shows that $a_{n+1} > a_n$ for all n, that is, *the sequence is steadily increasing.*

(c) *Existence of a Limit.* By Theorem 8.3.1, the sequence approaches a limit A; thus a_{n-1} and a_n both get arbitrarily close to A as n gets very large. Hence, A must satisfy the equation

$$A = \sqrt{3 + A};$$

solving, we have

$$A = \tfrac{1}{2}(1 + \sqrt{13}) \doteq 2.30.$$

Example 8.3.5. The sequence

$$u_1 = 1, \quad u_2 = 2, \quad u_3 = 3, \quad u_n = 2 + \frac{1}{n} \qquad (n > 3),$$

begins by increasing for three terms. However, this does not affect its ultimate behavior; after the third term, the sequence is bounded below by 2 and is monotonely decreasing. Hence it approaches (Theorem 8.3.2) a limit B (equal to 2 in this case).

Now, having discussed the properties of sequences, let us ask what types of problems give rise to a consideration of sequences. We shall consider three such types in the following sections.

8.4. SUM OF AN INFINITE SERIES

What meaning can we attach to the series $u_1 + u_2 + u_3 + \cdots$, where we never cease adding terms? Certainly this is not ordinary addition, which is only defined for a finite number of terms. We convert the problem to a problem in sequences by the following device. We define

$$\begin{aligned} s_1 &= u_1, \\ s_2 &= u_1 + u_2, \\ &\cdot \\ &\cdot \\ &\cdot \\ s_n &= u_1 + \cdots + u_n, \\ s_{n+1} &= u_1 + \cdots + u_n + u_{n+1}, \\ &\cdot \\ &\cdot \\ &\cdot \end{aligned}$$

The quantity s_n is called the nth partial sum of the series. Each value s_n is a well-defined number; so we have an infinite sequence of numbers s_1, s_2, s_3, . . .; to this sequence we can apply all the techniques and theorems concerning sequences and limits, as outlined in Sections 8.2 and 8.3. If we can show that the sequence $\{s_n\}$, $n = 1, 2, 3, \ldots$, approaches a limit A, *we shall define the sum of the infinite series to be A.*

Example 8.4.1. Consider the series $S = 1 + \frac{1}{2} + \frac{1}{4} + \frac{1}{8} + \frac{1}{16} + \cdots$. In this case,

$$s_n = 1 + \frac{1}{2^1} + \frac{1}{2^2} + \cdots + \frac{1}{2^{n-1}} = 2 - \frac{1}{2^{n-1}}.$$

Certainly the s_n's form a monotonely increasing sequence, since s_{n+1} is formed from s_n by the addition of the positive term 2^{-n}. Also, all the s_n are bounded above by 2; so the s_n approach a limit $A \leq 2$. Actually, in this instance $A = 2$, since s_n can be made as near to 2 as desired by making n large enough. Consequently, we have, by definition,

$$S = \lim_{n\to\infty} s_n = 2.$$

Example 8.4.2. Show that the series

$$S = 1 + \frac{1}{2} + \frac{1}{3} + \frac{1}{4} + \frac{1}{5} + \cdots + \frac{1}{n} + \cdots$$

does not have a sum according to the definition we have given. Here

$$s_1 = 1, \quad s_2 = 1 + \tfrac{1}{2}, \quad s_3 = 1 + \tfrac{1}{2} + \tfrac{1}{3}, \quad \ldots .$$

Consider the following partial sums:

$$s_1 = 1,$$

$$s_2 = 1 + \tfrac{1}{2} = \tfrac{3}{2},$$

$$\begin{aligned} s_4 &= 1 + \tfrac{1}{2} + \tfrac{1}{3} + \tfrac{1}{4} \\ &> 1 + \tfrac{1}{2} + \tfrac{1}{4} + \tfrac{1}{4} = 2, \end{aligned}$$

$$\begin{aligned} s_8 &= 1 + \tfrac{1}{2} + \tfrac{1}{3} + \tfrac{1}{4} + \tfrac{1}{5} + \tfrac{1}{6} + \tfrac{1}{7} + \tfrac{1}{8} \\ &> 1 + \tfrac{1}{2} + \tfrac{1}{4} + \tfrac{1}{4} + \tfrac{1}{8} + \tfrac{1}{8} + \tfrac{1}{8} + \tfrac{1}{8} \\ &= \tfrac{5}{2}, \end{aligned}$$

$$\begin{aligned} s_{16} &= 1 + \tfrac{1}{2} + \cdots + \tfrac{1}{16} \\ &> 1 + \tfrac{1}{2} + 2(\tfrac{1}{4}) + 4(\tfrac{1}{8}) + 8(\tfrac{1}{16}) \\ &= 3. \end{aligned}$$

Similarly,

$$S_{2^n} > 1 + n\left(\frac{1}{2}\right) = 1 + \frac{n}{2}.$$

This means that the sum of 2^n terms of the given series is greater than $1 + n/2$, that is, can be made *arbitrarily large* by taking enough terms.

This example illustrates the fact that the sum of an infinite series may not exist, even when the individual terms, from a certain stage onward, are all very small.

Infinite series in which each term is a function of x are often used to define functions. Consider

Example 8.4.3

$$f(x) = 1 + x + \frac{x^2}{2!} + \frac{x^3}{3!} + \cdots + \frac{x^n}{n!} + \cdots.$$

We take some fixed value of x, say x_1, in the range (0, 1). Now our series is

$$f(x_1) = 1 + x_1 + \frac{x_1^2}{2!} + \frac{x_1^3}{3!} + \cdots + \frac{x_1^n}{n!} + \cdots,$$

and all the terms are constants. We investigate the convergence of this series by considering the partial sums

$$s_1 = 1, \quad s_2 = 1 + x_1, \quad s_3 = 1 + x_1 + \frac{x_1^2}{2!}, \quad \ldots.$$

To investigate convergence, we evaluate ($m > n$):

$$|s_m - s_n| = \frac{x_1^{n+1}}{(n+1)!} + \frac{x_1^{n+2}}{(n+2)!} + \cdots + \frac{x_1^m}{m!}$$

$$\leq \frac{1}{(n+1)!} + \frac{1}{(n+2)!} + \cdots + \frac{1}{m!} + \cdots \qquad \text{(since } x_1 \leq 1\text{)}$$

$$\leq \frac{1}{(n+1)!} + \frac{1}{(n+1)!\,(n+2)} + \frac{1}{(n+1)!\,(n+2)^2} + \cdots$$

$$= \frac{1}{(n+1)!}\left[1 + \frac{1}{n+2} + \frac{1}{(n+2)^2} + \cdots\right]$$

$$= \frac{1}{(n+1)!}\,\frac{1}{1 - 1/(n+2)}$$

$$= \frac{n+2}{(n+1)(n+1)!}.$$

Now this quantity can be made arbitrarily small for n large enough. Hence (Theorem 8.3.3) the partial sums $s_1, s_2, s_3, \ldots$ approach a limit A, the value of which depends on x_1; so we denote this limit by $A(x_1)$. If we erect a vertical line at x_1, we can plot the partial sums $s_1, s_2, \ldots$ up this vertical line, and this will help to give a picture of the process (cf. Figure 8.4).

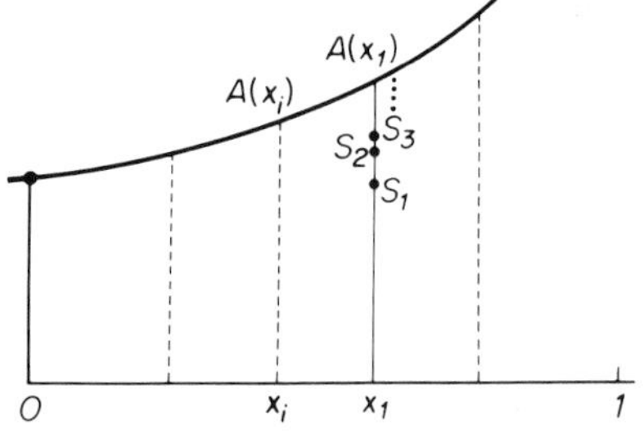

Figure 8.4

Now imagine that we repeat this procedure at points $x_2, x_3, \ldots$ (all of which are points in the range from 0 to 1), and that, for each x_i, we get a limit $A(x_i)$. If we join up all these limit points, we get a curve that represents a certain function of x; in this instance, the function is the exponential function e^x.

8.5. RATE OF CHANGE OF A FUNCTION AT A POINT

Given a function $y = f(x)$, how shall we define the rate of change of y with respect to x *at a specific point* x? Intuitively, we feel that the ratio (rise)/(run) provides us with some measure of the behavior of a function as exemplified in Figures 8.5, 8.6, 8.7, and 8.8.

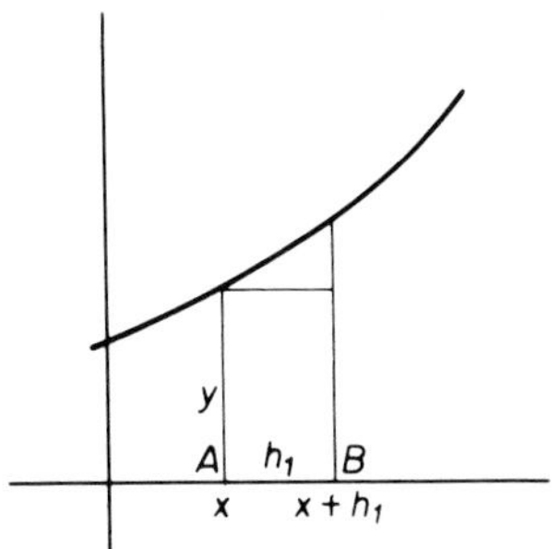

Figure 8.5

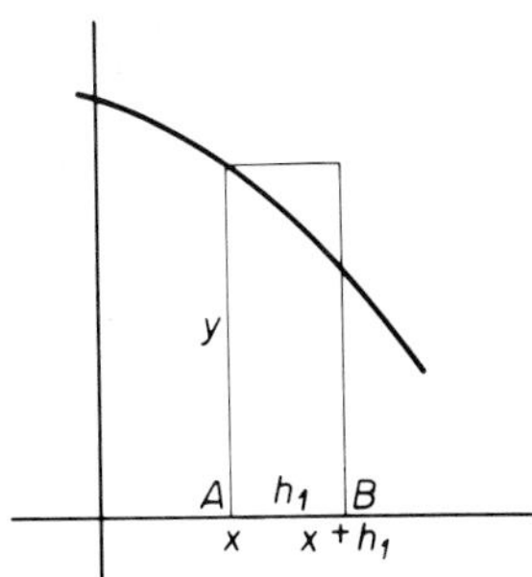

Figure 8.6

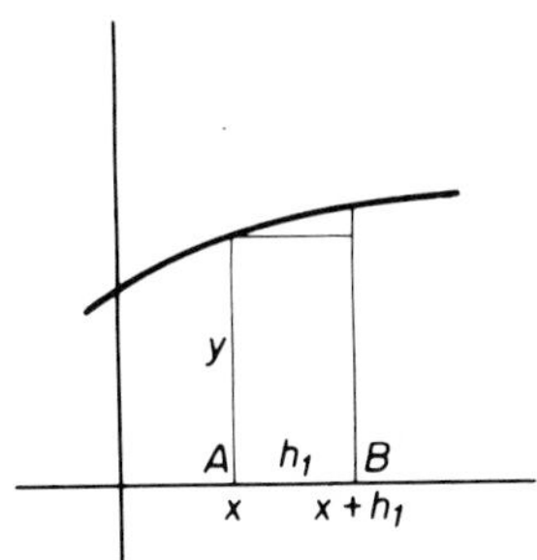

Figure 8.7

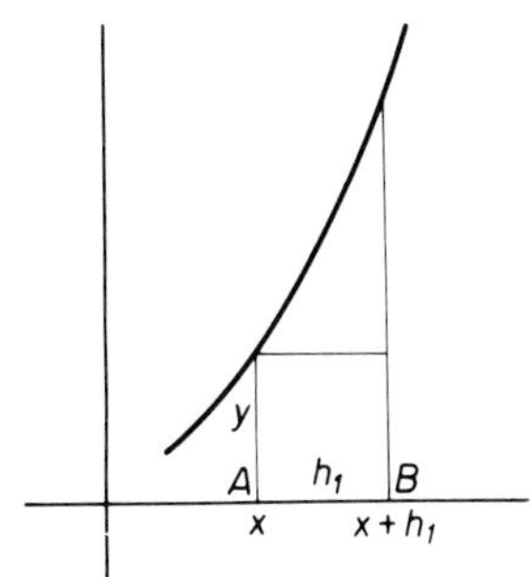

Figure 8.8

In Figure 8.5, the quotient

$$\frac{\text{positive rise}}{\text{positive run}}$$

implies that $f(x)$ is increasing, whereas, in Figure 8.6, the quotient

$$\frac{\text{negative rise}}{\text{positive run}}$$

implies that $f(x)$ is decreasing. Also, in Figure 8.7, we note that

$$\frac{\text{small rise}}{\text{positive run}}$$

implies that $f(x)$ is changing slowly; in Figure 8.8, the quotient

$$\frac{\text{large rise}}{\text{positive run}}$$

implies that $f(x)$ is changing rapidly.

Unfortunately, the quantities *rise* and *run* depend not only on the functional value at a particular point A but also on the functional value at a second point B, and so their ratio may not be a very reliable indicator of the situation at A. For example, in Figure 8.9, we find

$$\frac{\text{rise}}{\text{run}} = \frac{f(x + h_1) - f(x)}{h_1} = \frac{0}{h_1} = 0.$$

From this one computation, we would conclude that the rate of change of $f(x)$ at A, as measured by the quantity

$$\frac{\text{rise}}{\text{run}} = \frac{f(x + h_1) - f(x)}{h_1},$$

was zero, whereas we see from Figure 8.9 that $f(x)$ is increasing at A. What is the error in our procedure? The answer is that we chose *too large a base interval* h_1; let us choose a new (smaller) base interval h_2, and consider

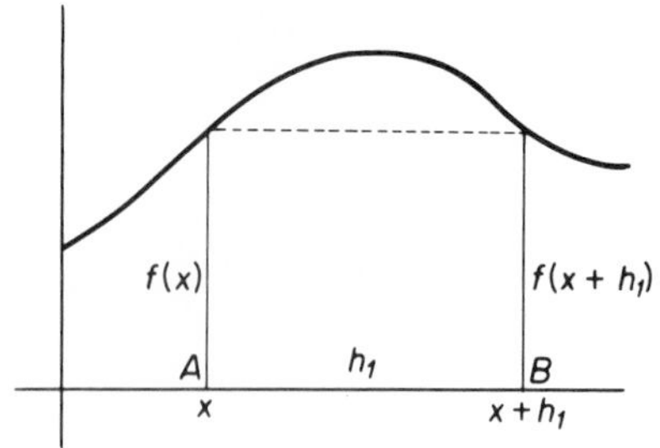

Figure 8.9

$$\frac{f(x + h_2) - f(x)}{h_2}$$

as a measure of what is going on at A. Again we encounter a similar difficulty; the quotient (rise)/(run) depends on h_2. So we are led to consider a sequence of numbers $h_1, h_2, h_3, \ldots$. Corresponding to each h_n, there is a value

$$u_n = \frac{f(x + h_n) - f(x)}{h_n}.$$

(Notice that x is fixed throughout this discussion.)

Our problem is now a problem in sequences: does the sequence $\{u_n\}$ approach a limit as h_n approaches 0? Notice that we *never* put $h_n = 0$ (to do so would produce a meaningless expression 0/0 for u_n). We are not interested in what happens to u_n when h_n *equals* 0; we only want to know how u_n behaves as h_n *approaches* zero.

If $f(x)$ is such a function that the ratio

$$\frac{f(x + h_n) - f(x)}{h_n}$$

approaches a limit as h_n approaches zero, we define the *derivative of* $f(x)$ *for this value of* x as being this limit. In symbols,

$$\frac{df(x)}{dx} = f'(x) = \lim_{h_n \to 0} \frac{f(x + h_n) - f(x)}{h_n}.$$

Example 8.5.1

$$\frac{dx^3}{dx} = \lim_{h_n \to 0} \frac{(x + h_n)^3 - x^3}{h_n} \qquad \text{(Step 1)}$$

$$= \lim_{h_n \to 0} \frac{x^3 + 3x^2h_n + 3xh_n^2 + h_n^3 - x^3}{h_n} \qquad \text{(Step 2)}$$

$$= \lim_{h_n \to 0} (3x^2 + 3xh_n + h_n^2) \qquad \text{(Step 3)}$$

$$= 3x^2. \qquad \text{(Step 4)}$$

Notice that division by h_n was permissible in going from Step 2 to Step 3 since h_n is *never* equal to zero.

Example 8.5.2. Find $f'(x)$, given $f(x) = \sqrt{x}$.
Here

$$f'(x) = \lim_{h_n \to 0} \frac{\sqrt{x + h_n} - \sqrt{x}}{h_n}$$

$$= \lim_{h_n \to 0} \frac{\sqrt{x + h_n} - \sqrt{x}}{h_n} \frac{\sqrt{x + h_n} + \sqrt{x}}{\sqrt{x + h_n} + \sqrt{x}}$$

$$= \lim_{h_n \to 0} \frac{h_n}{h_n(\sqrt{x + h_n} + \sqrt{x})}$$

$$= \lim_{h_n \to 0} \frac{1}{\sqrt{x + h_n} + \sqrt{x}}$$

$$= \frac{1}{2\sqrt{x}}.$$

We might conclude this section by noting that we have defined the rate of change of the function $y = f(x)$ with respect to x as being the limit (if the limit exists) of the ratio

$$\frac{f(x + h_n) - f(x)}{h_n}$$

as h_n approaches zero. If we interpret $f(x)$ as being distance, and x as being time, then this provides us with the definition of *velocity at a point.* We are only entitled to speak of velocity at a point when the function that expresses distance traversed as a function of time is such that

$$\lim_{h_n \to 0} \frac{f(x + h_n) - f(x)}{h_n}$$

exists. Such a function is said to be differentiable at x.

EXERCISES

1. Use the method of Example 8.5.1 to find the derivative $f'(x)$ in case

   (a) $f(x) = x^2 - 4x + 5$, (b) $f(x) = 1/(x + 6)$,

   (c) $f(x) = x^4$, (d) $f(x) = (2 - 3x)/(5 - 4x)$.

2. Find $f'(x)$, given that

   (a) $f(x) = \sqrt{3x^2 + 1}$, (b) $f(x) = 1/(\sqrt{1 - 5x})$.

8.6. AREA UNDER A CURVE

The third problem to be considered is that which arises when we try to define what we mean by "area under a curve". Consider the curve that represents the function $y = f(x)$, and let us try to define the area formed by the verticals ad, bc, the x-axis, and the curve (Figure 8.10).

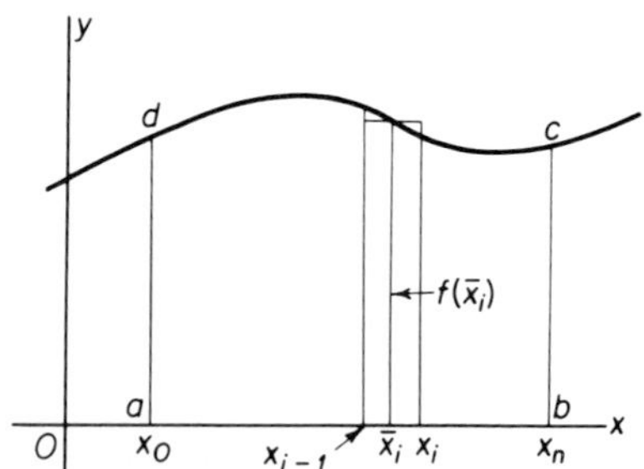

Figure 8.10

Intuition suggests that we should

(a) partition the range from a to b by points $x_0, x_1, \ldots, x_n$;

(b) within each subinterval (x_{i-1}, x_i), choose a point $\bar{x}_i$;

(c) evaluate $f(\bar{x}_i)$;

(d) form the product $f(\bar{x}_i)(x_i - x_{i-1})$;

(e) form the sum

$$S_n = \sum_{i=1}^{n} f(\bar{x}_i)(x_i - x_{i-1}).$$

This sum S_n, which is the sum of the areas of n rectangles, will give us an approximation to the "area under the curve".

Again we convert the area problem into a problem on sequences by considering a sequence of partitions $\pi_1, \pi_2, \pi_3, \ldots$ with the property that the length of the greatest sub-interval in the partition π_n approaches zero as n approaches infinity (increases beyond any bound). Corresponding to each partition π_n, there is a sum $S(\pi_n)$, and we concentrate on the behavior of the $S(\pi_n)$'s. If, as n approaches infinity, the $S(\pi_n)$ approach a limit A, then we *define* the area under the curve as being that limit A. An elementary application of this procedure to find an area is given in

Example 8.6.1. Consider $f(x) = 1 + x^2$ in the interval $(0, 1)$ (cf. Figure 8.11). We compute

$$f(0) = 1,$$
$$f\left(\frac{1}{n}\right) = 1 + \left(\frac{1}{n}\right)^2,$$
$$f\left(\frac{2}{n}\right) = 1 + \left(\frac{2}{n}\right)^2,$$
$$\cdots\cdots\cdots\cdots\cdots\cdots$$
$$f\left(\frac{n-1}{n}\right) = 1 + \left(\frac{n-1}{n}\right)^2.$$

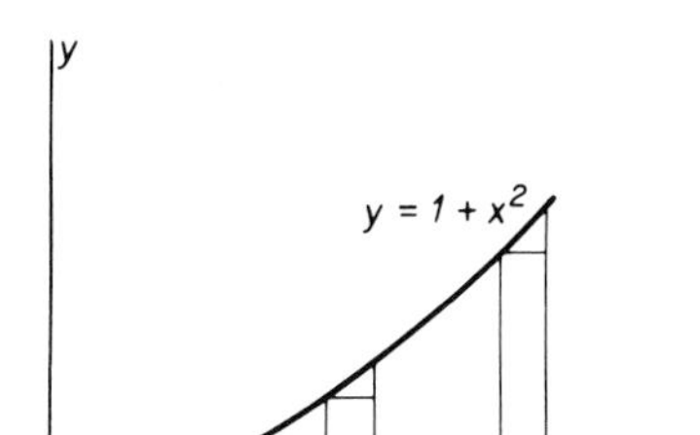

Figure 8.11

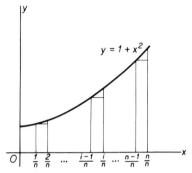

Then the area of all the n rectangles is given by

$$\begin{aligned}
S_n &= \left(\frac{1}{n}\right)f(0) + \left(\frac{1}{n}\right)f\left(\frac{1}{n}\right) + \cdots + \left(\frac{1}{n}\right)f\left(\frac{n-1}{n}\right) \\
&= \left(\frac{1}{n}\right)\left[1 + \left(1 + \frac{1^2}{n^2}\right) + \left(1 + \frac{2^2}{n^2}\right) + \cdots + \left(1 + \frac{(n-1)^2}{n^2}\right)\right] \\
&= \left(\frac{1}{n}\right)\left[n + \frac{1}{n^2}\{1^2 + 2^2 + \cdots + (n-1)^2\}\right] \\
&= \left(\frac{1}{n}\right)\left[n + \frac{1}{n^2}\left\{\frac{(n-1)(n)(2n-1)}{6}\right\}\right] \\
&= \left(\frac{1}{n}\right)\left[\frac{6n^2 + (n-1)(2n-1)}{6n}\right] \\
&= \frac{8n^2 - 3n + 1}{6n^2}.
\end{aligned}$$

To obtain the area under the curve, we let the width of each rectangle approach zero (that is, the number of rectangles $n \longrightarrow \infty$); then

$$\lim_{n\to\infty} S_n = \lim_{n\to\infty} \frac{8n^2 - 3n + 1}{6n^2}$$

$$= \lim_{n\to\infty} \frac{8 - (3/n) + (1/n^2)}{6}$$

$$= \frac{8}{6} = \frac{4}{3} = \text{area under the curve.}$$

EXERCISES

1. Use the method of this section to find the area bounded by the lines $x = 0$, $y = 0$ $x = 2$, and the curve $y = f(x)$, where

   (a) $f(x) = 1 + x + x^3$, (b) $f(x) = 2 + x + x^2$.

9

Probability Theory and Statistics

by David A. Sprott

9.1. INTRODUCTION

Inferences are either deductive or inductive. Deductive inferences are based on reasoning from general assumptions to particular conclusions, from axioms to theorems or propositions (as in Euclid), from the population to the sample drawn from the population. The population is the totality of observations in all relevant respects like the observations of the sample; the population may be finite or infinite, hypothetical or real. It might be well for the reader to consider here the following example (the situation is used again in Example 9.2.1).

Example 9.1.1. A certain machine is producing rivets under fixed conditions; a sample is taken and the diameters of all rivets in the sample are measured.

Here the parent population is the collection of all rivets produced, being produced, or to be produced in the future by the machine under the set conditions. Presumably, the number of possible rivet diameters is a very large number U. While U is enormous (or may be enormous), it is finite. If n is the number of rivets in the sample, n might be only 50 or 100.

The purpose of deductive reasoning is to reveal the consequences of a set of axioms; Euclidean geometry is an excellent example of this procedure, although most mathematical arguments are essentially deductive. Three main characteristics of deductive reasoning are:

(a) If the logic is correct, the inference is certainly true.

(b) No knowledge about the real world can be obtained solely by deductive reasoning.

(c) An inference is valid whether or not all the axioms were used in arriving at it.

Inductive inferences are based on reasoning from particular cases to general conclusions, from a sample to the population from which the sample came, from observations to a general law. Scientific inferences are inductive, although they usually contain many deductive steps. Three main characteristics of inductive reasoning are:

(a) If the logic and observations are correct, the inferences are still uncertain, that is, there is always a chance that they are erroneous.

(b) Inductive reasoning is the reasoning by which knowledge of the real world is obtained.

(c) Inductive inferences based on a subset of the available data are necessarily suspect (otherwise anything could be "proved" statistically by selection of the evidence).

Statistics is the study of inductive inference.

For convenience and clarification, the study of statistics can be subdivided as follows:

1. *Design* or logical structure of experiments.
2. *Statistical analysis* or extraction of information from the resulting data.

Statistical analysis includes

(a) *Study of populations.*

(b) *Study of variations.*

(c) *Reduction of data* by

(1) *specification of populations* (mathematical models),
(2) *estimation, and criteria of estimation,*
(3) *study of distributions.*

The design of an experiment refers to the actual method of carrying out the experiment in such a way as to ensure that the resulting data will contain the information wanted. If they do not, all subsequent statistical analysis will be worthless; proper experimental design is therefore a prerequisite for statistical analysis.

Statistics includes the study of populations, since any measurement can be considered as one of a hypothetical population consisting of the totality of all similar measurements. Statistics as the study of variation arises from the study of populations; the actual measurement of variation is an important reason for carrying out an experiment. Statistics as the reduction of data is necessary in order to reduce many observations to a few relevant measures; under this heading come:

(1) the choice of the mathematical form of the population;
(2) estimation of any unknown quantities (parameters) occurring in this mathematical model of the population;
(3) distributions, that is, deduction of the exact nature of variation in random samples from the population.

Since inductive inferences are statements of uncertainty, the study of statistics must begin with the study of the theory of mathematical probability (which is strictly deductive). In Section 9.2, we shall consider a typical set of experimental data, and in Section 9.3, we shall discuss the ideas of mathematical probability needed to analyze such data.

9.2. SAMPLING FROM A POPULATION

Let us return to the situation described in Example 9.1.1; there we have a machine producing rivets, and we consider this *parent population* of rivets. Suppose that the diameters of all rivets in the parent population are given by

$$d_1, d_2, d_3, \ldots, d_U.$$

Then we can define the *population mean* by the equation

$$\mu = \frac{1}{U}(d_1 + d_2 + d_3 + \cdots + d_U),$$

and the *population variance* by the equation

$$\sigma^2 = \frac{1}{U-1}[(d_1 - \mu)^2 + (d_2 - \mu)^2 + \cdots + (d_U - \mu)^2].$$

In general, these two equations define μ and σ^2 for any population of quantities d_i. These two constants are descriptive of the population; μ is the familiar "average value", whereas σ^2 is the average squared deviation of the diameters d_i from μ.

It is clear that μ and σ^2 can never be known in most cases since, if U is at all large, it would be quite impossible to measure all the quantities d_i (of course, there are a few biological populations where U is small enough that μ and σ^2 can actually be found). This consideration leads us to consider taking only a few items from the parent population to form a *random sample.*

When we say that a sample is random, we are indulging in wishful thinking since it is likely that no sample is ever truly random. Intuitively, a random sample is one in whose selection we have attempted to avoid any discernible pattern. For example, we might not be obtaining a random sample of American men if we selected only Republicans; we might not get a random sample of incomes if we selected only those home-owners who lived on street corners; we might not get a random sample of rivets if we always took a sample just before shift change or if we always took our sample at 10 A.M. Wednesdays; we might not get a random sample of vegetables grown in a field if we selected our sample only from one small area on the south side of the field. Even if we have, as far as we think possible, achieved randomness, we may have neglected some pattern factor. The most we can do is strive for randomness; like complete perfection, complete randomness will tend to elude us.

However, suppose we have taken from a parent population a sample of rivet diameters; the number of elements in the sample would be a relatively small number N (N might be 200 or 300). Then, if we denote the rivet diameters in the sample by

$$x_1, x_2, x_3, \ldots, x_N,$$

we can define the *sample mean* as

$$\bar{x} = \frac{1}{N}(x_1 + x_2 + \cdots + x_N),$$

and the *sample variance* as

$$s^2 = \frac{1}{N-1}[(x_1 - \bar{x})^2 + (x_2 - \bar{x})^2 + \cdots + (x_N - \bar{x})^2].$$

Note that we could define these quantities in any way we wanted to; we select our definitions so that they will be useful later.

We will now take note of the difference between the *population parameters* μ and σ^2 and the corresponding *sample parameters* $\bar{x}$ and s^2. The former are constants, but generally unknown and unknowable; the latter are variables (since they will undoubtedly change somewhat if you select another sample), but can be easily computed.

Let us consider a numerical example.

Example 9.2.1. A certain machine is producing rivets under fixed production conditions. A sample of nine rivets is taken, and the rivet diameters are measured as 13.42, 13.56, 13.48, 13.48, 13.55, 13.59, 13.59, 13.51, 13.48 mm. Find the sample mean and sample variance of the rivet diameters.

Here

$$\bar{x} = \frac{\sum x_i}{9} = \frac{x_1 + x_2 + \cdots + x_9}{9}$$

$$= \frac{121.46}{9} = 13.49555556.$$

$$8s^2 = \sum_{i=1}^{9} (x_i - \bar{x})^2$$

$$= \sum_{i=1}^{9} x_i^2 - 2\bar{x} \sum_{i=1}^{9} x_i + 9\bar{x}^2$$

$$= \sum_{i=1}^{9} x_i^2 - 9\bar{x}^2$$

$$= 1639.2040 - 1639.1701789$$

$$= .0338211.$$

$$s^2 = .00422764.$$

[Note the result of premature rounding; a careless student might round his answer to $\bar{x} = 13.50$, and then find $8s^2 = 1639.20 - 1640.25 = -1.05$. This truly remarkable result ($8s^2$, being a *sum of squares*, must be positive) is typical of the results to be expected from "keeping two decimals"; even keeping three decimals in $\bar{x}$ still produces a negative answer. It is important to keep an adequate number of figures in statistical computations.]

One might repeat that, in the preceding example, the parent population comprises all rivets produced by the machine under the given conditions; there are U such, where U could easily be several millions, and is unknown. Similarly,

$$\mu = \text{the mean of all } U \text{ rivet diameters}$$

is an unknown parameter; and

$$\sigma^2 = \text{the variance of all } U \text{ rivet diameters}$$

is an unknown parameter.

One of the fundamental problems of statistics is to make (uncertain) inferences about μ and σ^2 (whose exact values remain unknown) from the observational knowledge acquired from the sample taken where it was found that $\bar{x} = 13.49555556$, $s^2 = .00422764$. This is referred to as the problem of *estimation*; we find the sample parameters and attempt to estimate the population parameters.

EXERCISES

1. Find the mean and variance of the following sample of rivet diameters.

12.62, 12.48, 12.53, 12.71, 12.60, 12.29, 12.47, 12.72,
12.54, 12.37, 12.58, 12.47, 12.43, 12.60, 12.42, 12.49.

2. Prove that if a sample $x_1, x_2, \ldots, x_N$ is given with sample mean $\bar{x}$ and sample variance s^2, then, in general

$$(N - 1)s^2 = \sum_{j=1}^{N} x_j^2 - \frac{1}{N}\left(\sum_{j=1}^{N} x_j\right)^2.$$

3. Show that in the parent population $d_1, d_2, \ldots, d_U$, with mean μ and variance σ^2, the following relation holds:

$$(U - 1)\sigma^2 = \sum_{j=1}^{U} d_j^2 - \frac{1}{U}\left(\sum_{j=1}^{U} d_j\right)^2.$$

9.3. SOME BASIC PROBLEMS OF STATISTICS

In general, we can obtain information about the particular sample we have selected; but we want information about the underlying parent population. This attempt to reason backward from the particular sample to the general population, to obtain some sort of (uncertain) knowledge of the world about us, generates all the problems of statistics. The first and most basic problem is to design the statistical experiment properly; for we can never obtain information from an experiment unless it has been designed so as to contain the desired information. *Experimental Design* is one of the more difficult branches of statistics conceptually, since many non-statisticians feel that all they need to do is collect a mass of numbers, call in a mathematician, and relax while he extracts information from the numbers. But what if the information is not there? Sir Ronald Fisher has pointed out that calling in a statistician *after* an experiment has been performed is like asking him to perform a *post mortem*; he may be able to tell what the experiment died of. But he can not create information not contained in the data; he should have been called in before the experiment so that he could plan beforehand how to analyze the data, and consequently decide on what data should be collected to provide the required information.

It might be worthwhile to make some remarks concerning the vast accumulation of numbers which present themselves as "government statistics". The word *statistics* derives from the word *state*; originally, it meant any data concerning the state, and consequently included census information and the like. This use of the word is now really obsolete; masses of governmental data should merely be called data (or *vital statistics* if one must preserve the old custom); thus, the Dominion Bureau of Statistics might better be called the Dominion Bureau of Vital Statistics. The term *statistics* could then be restricted to that branch of mathematics where we use inductive inference to obtain probabilistic knowledge of the real world from observational data. In this connection, it might not be out of place to recall the wide gap which, according to A. L. Bowley, exists between official and academic statistics. Bowley claims that all official data should be accompanied by the following explanation.

(a) The terms used in the headings and margins of the table are all employed in a technical sense, known only to officers who compiled it, and which they are unable for official reasons to divulge.

(b) The sub-divisions of the table and region to which it refers have been changed since the last return was published.

(c) Before tabulation the data have been subjected to numerous adjustments, allowances, and other corrections, of a kind to vitiate any tests of significance which the reader may be tempted to apply to them.*

After *experimental design*, the second major problem of statistics is *data organization*; this involves mathematical computation and, in the simplest case, might merely amount to computing a sample mean and a sample variance as in Example 9.2.1. Intuitively, we feel that the sample mean $\bar{x}$ and the sample variance s^2 should be reasonably close to μ and σ^2 respectively, and actually one can prove a very important result to this effect; we might state it as

THEOREM 9.3.1. Under very general conditions, the average value of $\bar{x}$ (computed from a number k of samples) approaches μ as k becomes infinite; similarly, the average value of s^2 approaches σ^2.

Theorem 9.3.1 can be made even more quantitative, but it illustrates the sort of theorem which can connect samples and parent population.

Finally, after planning the experiment and organizing the results, one may wish to *test a hypothesis* (do the experimental results support or cast doubt upon some initial hypothesis?), or to estimate a parameter (for example, knowing $\bar{x}$ and σ^2, estimate μ). Both these problems will be illustrated in the last section of this chapter, and both involve forging a connecting link between sample and parent population. This connecting link is supplied by the mathematical theory of probability, which will be introduced in the next section.

---

* Quoted by R. A. Fisher in his Presidential Address to the First Session of the Indian Statistical Conference, Calcutta, 1938 (Sankhya 4, 1938, pp. 14–17).

EXERCISES

1. Take 100 one-inch squares of white paper and write numbers on them so as to have two squares with 1 written on each, four squares with 2, five squares with 3, ten squares with 4, thirty-two squares with 5, twenty squares with 6, twelve squares with 7, nine squares with 8, six squares with 9. Compute μ and σ^2 for this parent population.

2. Mix the 100 squares of Exercise 1 in a paper bag. Draw out a sample of five squares, and compute the sample mean and sample variance; record these. Then replace the five squares, mix well, and draw a second sample. Repeat until you have recorded fifty samples.

3. Compute the average sample mean, namely,

$$\frac{\text{sum of 50 sample means}}{50},$$

and the average sample variance, namely,

$$\frac{\text{sum of 50 sample variances}}{50},$$

and compare these values with μ and σ^2.

9.4. PROBABILITY THEORY

The probability that a particular element of a population should have property A is said to be p if the following conditions are fulfilled.

[1] There is a reference set (population), hypothetical or real, of elements for each of which it is possible to know whether it has or has not property A; those elements possessing property A form a fraction p of the whole.

[2] It is known that the particular element in question is a member of the reference set.

[3] The particular element must not be a member of a recognizable subset in which elements possessing property A occur with a different relative frequency $p' \neq p$.

If there is a sample of n elements, and if property A occurs a times, then an estimate of p is a/n if the above conditions are satisfied. Sometimes a/n is called a statistical or empirical probability and p is called the theoretical probability. This is perhaps unfortunate terminology, since there is only one kind of mathematical probability; p is the probability, and a/n is an estimate of p based on a particular sample of size n.

Note that, since an element either does or does not possess property A, we must have

$$Pr(A) + Pr\,(\text{not } A) = 1.$$

Thus the total probability is unity.

It should be pointed out that the theoretical probability is seldom known (although sometimes assumed), whereas its estimate a/n is an observation, and will change from sample to sample.

For example, one usually considers the probability of obtaining heads on the tossing of a coin to be $\frac{1}{2}$; however, this is an arbitrary *assumption.* All that can be said is that the probability of obtaining heads is some number p between 0 and 1. If the coin is actually tossed 1000 times and 460 heads occur, the estimate of p, *as determined by this sample*, is then .46. Naturally, a different experiment would likely produce a different estimate of p.

The foregoing probabilities are sometimes called *marginal*, to distinguish them from *conditional probabilities*.

Conditional Probability: The *conditional probability*, written $Pr(A \mid B)$, is the probability of occurrence of A, when A belongs to the recognizable subset of events (A, B) in which B is *known* to have occurred. Suppose that out of a total of n elements, there are a elements with property A, b with property B, and c with properties A and B simultaneously; then

$$Pr(A) = \frac{a}{n}; \qquad Pr(B) = \frac{b}{n}.$$

$$Pr(A, B) = \text{the joint probability of } A \text{ and } B = \frac{c}{n}.$$

If an element is known to have property B, then it belongs to a recognizable subset in which $Pr(A \mid B) = c/b$. We might note that

$$Pr(A \mid B)Pr(B) = \frac{c}{b} \cdot \frac{b}{n} = \frac{c}{n} = Pr(A, B).$$

Conditional probabilities are rather difficult to deal with, and we shall not use them in our illustrations.

Before taking up some examples, we shall establish two very basic theorems.

THEOREM 9.4.1. If two events A and B are *independent*, that is, if the occurrence of A does not affect B, then

$$Pr(AB) = Pr(A)Pr(B),$$

where we use $Pr(AB)$ to denote the probability of the joint occurrence of A and B.

Proof. Let A occur a times in n trials; let the separate event B occur b times in m trials. We can then think of nm compound events (each occurrence or non-occurrence of A paired with each occurrence or non-occurrence of B); among these nm compound events, ab are occurrences of both A and B. So

$$Pr(AB) = \frac{ab}{nm} = \frac{a}{n} \cdot \frac{b}{m} = Pr(A)Pr(B).$$

The probability occurring in Theorem 9.4.1 is sometimes called "both-and" probability.

THEOREM 9.4.2. If two events A and B are *mutually exclusive*, that is, if they can not both occur together, then

$$Pr(A \cup B) = Pr(A) + Pr(B),$$

where we use the cup notation $\cup$ to mean "or"; thus, $Pr(A \cup B)$ refers to the occurrence of either A or B.

Proof. Suppose that in n trials, event A occurs a times and event B occurs b times. Then "either A or B" will occur $a + b$ times, and

$$Pr(A \cup B) = \frac{a + b}{n} = \frac{a}{n} + \frac{b}{n} = Pr(A) + Pr(B).$$

The probability in Theorem 9.4.2 is sometimes called "either-or" probability.

Example 9.4.1. Find the probability of (a) drawing a spade from a deck of cards; (b) tossing a 3 or a 4 with a die.

In (a), the entire population comprises 52 cards of which 13 are spades; so the theoretical probability of drawing a spade is $\frac{13}{52}$.

In (b), let A = tossing a 3, B = tossing a 4; then

$$Pr(A \cup B) = \tfrac{1}{6} + \tfrac{1}{6} = \tfrac{1}{3}.$$

Example 9.4.2. A deck of cards is well shuffled; find the probability that the king and queen of hearts are together.

Here the entire population consists of all 52! shuffles; if the king and queen of hearts are together, they can be considered a single card (2 ways), and so the number of shuffles in which they lie together is 2(51)! The required probability then is $2(51)!/52! = \frac{1}{26}$.

Example 9.4.3. A die is tossed four times; find the probability that a three shows up at least once in these four tosses.

Probability of no three on a single toss $= \frac{5}{6}$.

Probability of no three on four tosses (Theorem 9.4.1) $= (\frac{5}{6})^4$.

Total probability = 1.

Hence, the probability of at least one three is

$$1 - \text{probability of no three} = 1 - (\tfrac{5}{6})^4 = \tfrac{671}{1296}.$$

Example 9.4.4. Assuming that all sex distributions in a family are equally likely, find the probability that a family of four children contains all boys, given that it contains at least one boy.

This is an example of conditional probability. Let A be the event that a family of four contains four boys, B be the event that a family of four contains at least one boy. Then

$$Pr(B) = 1 - Pr(\text{Family contains 4 girls})$$
$$= 1 - \left(\frac{1}{2}\right)^4 = \frac{15}{16}.$$
$$Pr(A) = \left(\frac{1}{2}\right)^4 = \frac{1}{16}.$$
$$Pr(A \mid B) = \frac{Pr(A, B)}{Pr(B)} = \frac{\frac{1}{16}}{\frac{15}{16}} = \frac{1}{15}.$$

Example 9.4.5. If two cards are selected at random from an ordinary deck, the probability that the first is a spade is $\frac{13}{52}$. The probability that the second is a heart is then $\frac{13}{51}$. Hence, the joint probability of a spade and a heart (in that order) is

$$\frac{13}{52} \cdot \frac{13}{51} = \frac{169}{2652}.$$

If the order of occurrence is irrelevant, then a spade and heart can occur in two mutually exclusive ways; so the total probability is

$$\frac{169}{2652} + \frac{169}{2652} = \frac{169}{1326}.$$

Example 9.4.6. Seven balls are tossed into four numbered boxes so that each ball falls into a box and is equally likely to fall into any of the boxes. What is the probability that the first box will contain two balls?

The probability that a ball falls into the first box is $\frac{1}{4}$; so the probability that two balls fall into the first box is $(\frac{1}{4})^2$. The probability that a ball does not fall into the first box is $\frac{3}{4}$, and so the probability that five balls do not is $(\frac{3}{4})^5$. Since two balls can be selected from seven in ${}_7C_2 = \binom{7}{2}$ mutually exclusive ways, then the total required probability is

$$\binom{7}{2}\left(\frac{1}{4}\right)^2\left(\frac{3}{4}\right)^5 = \frac{21(3)^5}{4^7} = \frac{5103}{16384}.$$

Example 9.4.7. A, B, and C throw a die over and over again in that order; the first one to throw a six wins 50 dollars. Find the probability that C wins.

C may win on the third or sixth or ninth, et cetera, throws. To win on the third throw, A must lose, *and* B must lose, *and* C must win; the probability of this is

$$\left(\frac{5}{6}\right)^2 \frac{1}{6}.$$

To win on the sixth throw, the first five throws must be losses and the sixth throw must be a win; the probability of this is

$$\left(\frac{5}{6}\right)^5 \left(\frac{1}{6}\right).$$

Continue this argument, and then add the probabilities of these mutually exclusive events to find

$$\begin{aligned} Pr(C \text{ wins}) &= \left(\frac{5}{6}\right)^2 \frac{1}{6} + \left(\frac{5}{6}\right)^5 \frac{1}{6} + \left(\frac{5}{6}\right)^8 \frac{1}{6} + \cdots \\ &= \frac{(\frac{5}{6})^2 \frac{1}{6}}{1 - (\frac{5}{6})^3} \\ &= \frac{5^2}{6^3 - 5^3} = \frac{25}{91}. \end{aligned}$$

EXERCISES

1. The numbers $1, 2, \ldots, n$ are arranged in random order. Find the probability that the digits (a) 1 and 2, (b) 1, 2, and 3, appear as neighbours in the order named.
   Answers: (a) $1/n$, (b) $1/n(n-1)$.

2. Show that it is more probable to get at least one ace with four dice than at least one double ace in 24 throws of two dice.

3. What is the probability that a five-card hand will contain exactly two aces? At least two aces?
   Answers: $\binom{4}{2}\binom{48}{3}\Big/\binom{52}{5}$, $\left[\binom{4}{2}\binom{48}{3} + \binom{4}{3}\binom{48}{2} + \binom{48}{1}\right]\Big/\binom{52}{2}$.

4. Given that a throw with ten dice produces at least one ace, what is the probability p of two or more aces?
   Answer: $1 - 10(5)^9/(6^{10} - 5^{10})$.

5. In a bridge game, West has no ace. What is the probability of his partner's having (a) no ace, (b) two or more aces?
   Answers: (a) $\binom{35}{13}\Big/\binom{39}{13} = .182$; (b) The probability of exactly one ace is $4\binom{35}{12}\Big/\binom{36}{12} = .411$; answer $= 1 - .182 - .411 = .407$.

6. In a bolt factory, machines A, B, C, manufacture respectively 25%, 35%, and 40% of the total. Of their outputs, 5%, 4%, and 2% are defective bolts. A bolt is drawn at random from the produce, and is found defective. What are the probabilities that it was manufactured by machines A, B, C?

Answers: $\frac{125}{345}, \frac{140}{345}, \frac{80}{345}$.

9.5. PROBABILITY DISTRIBUTIONS

Let k be an integer, $0 \leq k \leq n$; then a (discrete) probability distribution is a function $p(k)$ such that $p(k)$ gives the probability of the occurrence of k events in n trials. We note that

$$p(0) + p(1) + p(2) + \cdots + p(n) = 1.$$

Example 9.5.1. *The Binomial Distribution.* Consider n independent trials for each of which the probability of success is p and of failure is q $(p + q = 1)$. Then the probability of a particular pattern of exactly k successes and $n - k$ failures is $p^k q^{n-k}$; however, exactly k successes can occur in $\binom{n}{k}$ mutually exclusive ways, and so the probability of exactly k successes is

$$p(k) = \binom{n}{k} p^k q^{n-k}.$$

This distribution has occurred in previous examples. Note that

$$\begin{aligned} p(0) + p(1) + \cdots + p(n) \\ &= \binom{n}{0} q^n + \binom{n}{1} pq^{n-1} + \binom{n}{2} p^2 q^{n-2} + \cdots + \binom{n}{n} p^n \\ &= (p + q)^n = 1. \end{aligned}$$

For example, if we consider a perfect coin $(p = \frac{1}{2})$, then the probability of r successes in seven trials is given by

$$p(0) = \tfrac{1}{128}, \quad p(1) = \tfrac{7}{128}, \quad p(2) = \tfrac{21}{128}, \quad p(3) = \tfrac{35}{128},$$

$$p(4) = \tfrac{35}{128}, \quad p(5) = \tfrac{21}{128}, \quad p(6) = \tfrac{7}{128}, \quad p(7) = \tfrac{1}{128}.$$

Example 9.5.2. *The Hypergeometric Distribution.* Suppose a population of N elements contains D defectives; if a sample of n is drawn, find the probability that d defectives occur in the sample.

Here d defectives can be selected in $\binom{D}{d}$ ways, and the remaining $n - d$ non-defectives in the sample can be selected in $\binom{N - D}{n - d}$ ways.

Hence the total number of ways such a sample can be selected is $\binom{D}{d}\binom{N-D}{n-d}$. Since the total number of samples of size n is $\binom{N}{n}$, the required probability is

$$p(d) = \frac{\binom{D}{d}\binom{N-D}{n-d}}{\binom{N}{n}}.$$

This probability distribution, like that in the preceding example, contains unknown *parameters*, that is, p, q, N, D.

The *mean* of a distribution $p(k)$ (called the *population mean*) is defined as

$$0 \cdot p(0) + 1 \cdot p(1) + 2 \cdot p(2) + \cdots + n \cdot p(n) = \sum kp(k) = \mu.$$

The variance of a distribution $p(k)$ (the *population variance*) is defined as

$$(0-\mu)^2p(0) + (1-\mu)^2p(1) + (2-\mu)^2p(2) + \cdots + (n-\mu)^2p(n) = \sum (k-\mu)^2p(k) = \sigma^2.$$

We note that

$$\begin{aligned}\sigma^2 &= \sum (k^2 - 2k\mu + \mu^2)p(k)\\ &= \sum k^2p(k) - 2\mu \sum kp(k) + \mu^2 \sum p(k).\end{aligned}$$

However, $\sum kp(k) = \mu$ and $\sum p(k) = 1$; hence

$$\sigma^2 = \sum k^2p(k) - \mu^2.$$

We employ this result in

Example 9.5.3. Find the population mean and population variance for the binomial distribution of Example 9.5.1.

$$\begin{aligned}\mu = \sum kp(k) &= \binom{n}{1}q^{n-1}p + 2\binom{n}{2}q^{n-2}p^2 + 3\binom{n}{3}q^{n-3}p^3 + \cdots + n\binom{n}{n}p^n\\ &= nq^{n-1}p + n(n-1)q^{n-2}p^2\\ &\qquad + \frac{n(n-1)(n-2)}{1 \cdot 2}q^{n-3}p^3 + \cdots + \frac{n!}{(n-1)!}p^n\\ &= np\left[q^{n-1} + (n-1)q^{n-2}p + \frac{(n-1)(n-2)}{1 \cdot 2}q^{n-3}p^2 + \cdots + p^{n-1}\right]\\ &= np(q+p)^{n-1} = np(1)^{n-1} = np.\end{aligned}$$

The variance can be found by noting that $k^2 = k(k-1) + k$. Thus

$$\begin{aligned}\sum k^2p(k) &= \sum k(k-1)p(k) + \sum kp(k)\\ &= \sum k(k-1)p(k) + \mu.\end{aligned}$$

$$\begin{aligned}\sum k(k-1)p(k) &= 2\cdot 1\binom{n}{2}q^{n-2}p^2 + 3\cdot 2\binom{n}{3}q^{n-3}p^3 + \cdots + n(n-1)p^n\\ &= n(n-1)q^{n-2}p^2 + \frac{n(n-1)(n-2)}{1}q^{n-3}p^3\\ &\quad + \frac{n(n-1)(n-2)(n-3)}{1\cdot 2}q^{n-4}p^4 + \cdots + n(n-1)p^n\\ &= n(n-1)p^2\Big[q^{n-2} + (n-2)q^{n-3}p\\ &\quad + \frac{(n-2)(n-3)}{1\cdot 2}q^{n-4}p^2 + \cdots + p^{n-2}\Big]\\ &= n(n-1)p^2(q+p)^{n-2} = n(n-1)p^2.\end{aligned}$$

Hence

$$\sum k^2p(k) = n(n-1)p^2 + \mu = n(n-1)p^2 + np$$

and

$$\sigma^2 = \sum k^2p(k) - \mu^2 = np - np^2 = npq.$$

Thus the population mean and population variance for the binomial distribution are respectively $\mu = np$, $\sigma^2 = npq$.

We may use Example 9.5.3 to compute a population mean. Suppose that a coin were tossed 100 times; then the population mean would be $100p$ (p = probability of heads) whereas the sample might show 40 heads. Thus the number of heads in the sample differs from the population mean obtained by letting $p = \frac{1}{2}$, which is not surprising since it is unlikely that the probability p of obtaining heads is exactly $\frac{1}{2}$. If another sample of 100 tosses were taken, the new number of heads would undoubtedly differ from the previous sample mean (and also from 50, *even if* $p = \frac{1}{2}$).

EXERCISES

1. Consider n tosses of a die; write down the probability distribution $p(k)$ for k sixes in n tosses ($k = 0, 1, 2, \ldots, n$) for the cases $n = 5$ and $n = 6$.
2. Repeat Exercise 1 in the case of a perfect coin for $n = 5$ and $n = 6$.
3. Compute the probability distribution $p(k)$ for the case when one draws samples of size 4 from a population of size 1000 containing exactly three defective items.

9.6. STATISTICAL INFERENCE

The preceding sections have briefly outlined the basis of probability theory, which is purely deductive. For instance, if the parameters of any probability distribution were known, then the probability of observing any particular sample could be computed exactly. Thus, if the probability of obtaining heads when tossing a coin were known to be $\frac{1}{2}$, and if the coin were tossed 10 times, the probability of obtaining exactly k heads would be exactly $\binom{10}{k}\left(\frac{1}{2}\right)^{10}$, which can be calculated for any value of k. The probability of obtaining fewer than three heads would be

$$\left[\binom{10}{0}+\binom{10}{1}+\binom{10}{2}\right]\left(\frac{1}{2}\right)^{10}=(1+10+45)\left(\frac{1}{2}\right)^{10}=\frac{56}{2^{10}}=.054.$$

This is an example of deductive reasoning (from the population to the sample), as are all probability arguments.

In practice, however, the sample is usually observed, and it is necessary to infer something about the population from which the sample came. This is an inductive argument, and thus goes beyond probability theory; we are confronted by a problem of statistical inference. The general problem of statistical inference is more complicated, and we can only give a few simple examples here.

Example 9.6.1. *Test of a Hypothesis.* Suppose two pain-relieving drugs A and B were each tried on ten people, and that seven people reported A better than B and three people reported B better than A. Is this evidence that A was significantly preferred to B?

The mathematical description of the population would then be a binomial distribution with $n = 10$ trials with a probability p that A will be preferred to B in any one trial. Then

$$Pr(k)=\binom{10}{k}p^kq^{n-k}\qquad (q=1-p).$$

For the observed sample, $k = 7$, and

$$Pr(7)=\binom{10}{7}p^7q^3.$$

Consider the *null hypothesis* (that is, the hypothesis that there is no difference): drug A is indistinguishable from drug B. In the above population, this would imply $p = \frac{1}{2}$. So we compute what is known as the *relative likelihood function*, namely, the ratio of the value $Pr(7)$ would assume if the null hypothesis were true to the maximum possible value of $Pr(7)$. This relative likelihood function is

$$\frac{\binom{10}{7}\left(\frac{5}{10}\right)^7\left(\frac{5}{10}\right)^3}{\binom{10}{7}\left(\frac{7}{10}\right)^7\left(\frac{3}{10}\right)^3} = \frac{5^{10}}{7^7 3^3} = .44.$$

Since the relative likelihood of the sample, under the hypothesis $p = \frac{1}{2}$, is so large, there is not sufficient evidence to reject this hypothesis; hence we are not justified in concluding that drug A is preferred to drug B.

If, on the other hand, nine people reported drug A better, and only one person reported drug B better, the relative likelihood of $p = \frac{1}{2}$ is then

$$\frac{5^{10}}{9^9 1^1} = .025.$$

This could easily be regarded as sufficiently small to justify our claiming that the hypothesis $p = \frac{1}{2}$ is definitely unlikely, and that hence there is significant evidence that drug A is preferred to drug B.

In the next examples, we shall try to illustrate other sorts of statistical questions that may be asked and indicate the *sort* of answers that may be given.

Example 9.6.2. The copper content of an alloy produced by process A is measured five times, and the mean value of these five readings is 5.31%, the variance being .00725. The copper content of an alloy produced by process B is measured eight times, and the mean and variance are 5.42% and .00683 respectively. Is there a real difference in the copper content of the alloy when produced by the two processes?

Here we set up a null hypothesis that the two batches of alloy do not differ, that is, there is a common theoretical mean μ. It is then possible (under very general assumptions) to compute a probability α so that we may say: Assuming no difference between the two batches of alloy, then the probability of the means differing as much as, or more than, they do (5.31 and 5.42) is α. If α turns out to be less than .05, we usually consider the hypothesis very unlikely and "reject it at the 95% level".

Example 9.6.3. *Estimation of Fiducial Limits.* The copper content of a certain alloy is measured as 5.25%, 5.36%, 5.29%, 5.43%, 5.22%. What can we say about the value μ of the copper content of the parent alloy?

Procedure here is to compute the mean of the sample as $26.55/5 = 5.31\%$; the variance is then

$$\frac{.06^2 + .05^2 + .02^2 + .12^2 + .09^2}{4} = .00725.$$

It is then possible, under very general assumptions, to compute a number b such that there is a 95% probability that the theoretical mean μ lies within the interval $5.31 - b$ to $5.31 + b$ (called a 95% fiducial interval). Notice that we can never give a certain answer in statistics; our answer must be phrased in probability language; for example,

$$Pr(5.31 - b \leq \mu \leq 5.31 + b) = .95.*$$

Example 9.6.4. *Estimation.* If a coin is tossed $n = 20$ times and heads occur 13 times, what can be said about p, the probability of obtaining heads in a single toss of that coin?

Here, the likelihood of p, knowing the observations, is

$$\binom{20}{13} p^{13} q^{7},$$

which attains its maximum when $p = \frac{13}{20} = .65$. This is called the *maximum likelihood estimate* of p, that is, the value of p that makes most probable what was actually observed. The maximum value of the likelihood is

$$\binom{20}{13}\left(\frac{13}{20}\right)^{13}\left(\frac{7}{20}\right)^{7} = \binom{20}{13}(.65)^{13}(.35)^{7}.$$

Thus, the relative likelihood of any value of p is

$$\frac{p^{13}q^{7}}{(.65)^{13}(.35)^{7}}.$$

We find that $p = .35$ makes the relative likelihood .024, and $p = .9$ makes it .01. Values of p outside of the range (.35, .9) are therefore unlikely, and can be disregarded. Thus the estimate is .65, with the true value very likely in the range $.35 \leq p \leq .9$. This range could be narrowed considerably by increasing n.

It should be noted that, in both Example 9.6.1 and Example 9.6.4, the final statements are not in terms of mathematical probability, but in terms of a quantity called likelihood. In certain cases, estimates can be given a probability interval (cf. Example 9.6.3), but the theory of probability is not always capable of measuring the uncertainty in an inductive inference.

---

* Some modern mathematicians object to this statement, using the argument that μ is a number, and, as such, can have no objective frequency distribution associated with it. Thus, according to them, for any given b, μ either is within the interval or outside of it. In the first case, the probability of the given inequality is unity; in the second case, it is zero. For most applications in science, this view seems unjustified; for a complete discussion, see R. A. Fisher, *Statistical Methods and Scientific Inference* (Edinburgh, Oliver and Boyd, 1956); see also *J. Roy. Statis. Soc.*, **17** (1955), pp. 69–78.

Also, in Examples 9.6.1 and 9.6.2, probability statements about the null hypothesis can not be made; probability statements are made only about events under the assumption of the null hypothesis. Thus, such tests of significance do not lead to probability statements about the real world, but only to a measure of reluctance to accept the hypothesis which leads to the probability statements.

10

Some Types of Geometry

by Gerald Berman

10.1. INTRODUCTION

During many centuries, the study of synthetic Euclidean geometry or "Euclid" was considered an indispensable part of classical education and an unrivalled exercise in logic, clear thinking, orderly presentation, and aesthetic appreciation. Even today, nearly every secondary school student learns about Euclidean geometry. Such a student usually absorbs the idea that Euclidean geometry is the geometry of our real world, the only possible type of geometry. This idea prevailed for many years, and it was only a little over a hundred years ago that it was discovered that other types of geometry are logically possible, and that a different one of these might possibly give a more accurate picture of the geometry of the real world.

In this chapter, we shall discuss a few of the geometries which are most closely connected with Euclidean geometry.

10.2. MATHEMATICAL SYSTEMS

First of all, let us say a word about logical mathematical systems; Euclidean geometry is a good example of such a system. We start with

points and lines, which we take as undefined quantities, and talk about an intuitively accepted relation of incidence between these points and lines. After stating a number of rules or axioms, and introducing appropriate definitions, various theorems are proved.

A similar point of view is taken in all modern mathematics; consequently, we might well regard Euclid as the first of modern mathematicians. Nearly every logical mathematical system contains undefined sets of elements, undefined relations, axioms, definitions, and theorems. Underlying any such system are the basic rules of deductive reasoning which are, of course, also assumptions.

10.3. SHORTCOMINGS IN EUCLID'S DEVELOPMENT

As we have stated, Euclid was the first to try to construct a logical mathematical system. Although he was very successful, his original development contained minor defects, some of which still persist in secondary school versions of Euclid. Most of these "defects" are in the direction of assuming certain deep axioms intuitively; some of these axioms, such as the axioms of order, seemed so clearly obvious to Euclid that he did not recognize them as axioms. Even today, many people prefer to base a development of Euclidean geometry on intuitive concepts of order rather than on an axiomatic formalism concerning order; such a formalism could confuse many students.

Euclid started out by defining points and lines:

a *point* is that which has no part;

a *line* is breadthless width.

Today we realize that these are not satisfactory definitions; they are merely intuitive descriptions. Nowadays, line and point are usually taken as undefined elements, and accepted intuitively.

The five axioms of Euclid were as follows.

I. A straight line may be drawn from any one point to any other point.
II. A finite straight line segment may be produced to any length in a straight line.
III. A circle may be described with any centre and at any distance from that centre (that is, with any radius).
IV. All right angles are equal.
V. If a straight line meets two other straight lines, so as to make the sum of the two interior angles on one side of it less than two right angles, the other straight lines will meet if produced on that side on which the sum of the angles is less than two right angles.

An examination of the proofs of the various theorems given by Euclid shows that he made several other *tacit* assumptions. For example, he assumed that geometric figures may be moved without distortion, and he nowhere explicitly stated any axioms relating to order among points on a line. We shall make a few remarks about these two ideas.

10.4. A THEOREM FROM EUCLID

The following theorem appears early in most presentations of Euclid.* It is a classical proposition of Euclid's Book I.

If two sides and the contained angle of one triangle are respectively equal to two sides and the contained angle of another triangle, the two triangles are congruent.

The proof certainly involves *moving* one of the triangles. It is known that in the "real" world, lengths change *during* motion. Although this notion seems intuitively impossible, it does now have acceptance, and two new verifications have been published very recently. Thus, invariance of geometric figures under rigid motion, as used in Euclid, is an assumption which should be explicitly stated.

As a matter of fact, it is probable that the geometry of the real world is hyperbolic rather than Euclidean (see Section 10.7); in the real world, the sum of the angles of a triangle is probably very very slightly less than 180°. However, this fact in no way affects Euclidean geometry as a deductive mathematical system; it is still one of the most valuable examples of a formal deductive system, it is still an integral part of mathematics (since mathematics is concerned with abstract systems and not with physical reality), and it is a close enough approximation to physical reality to be an adequate description of all situations which arise in ordinary everyday life.

10.5. A PARADOX

The following paradox illustrates the need for order axioms in Euclidean geometry. A careful redrawing of the figures involved will point up the flaw in the "proof". But there is no explicit assumption in Euclid which takes care of the situation.

THEOREM. *Every triangle is isosceles.*

Proof. In the triangle ABC, let O be the point of intersection of the perpendicular bisector OD of side BC and the bisector AO of the angle A. Draw the line OE perpendicular to side AB and the line OF perpendicular to side AC, as shown in Figures 10.1 and 10.2 (Figure 10.1 corresponds to the case when O is inside the triangle; Figure 10.2 to the case when O is

---

* For example, cf. Lougheed and Workman, *Geometry for High Schools* (New York: The Macmillan Company, 1935), p. 57.

outside the triangle. Actually, it can be shown that O can not lie inside the triangle.) Join O to the points B and C.

Then the triangles AEO and AFO are congruent, and the triangles OBD and OCD are congruent. It follows at once that $EO = OF$ and $OB = OC$; hence the right-angled triangles OEB and OFC are also congruent. The theorem then follows since we now have $AE = AF$ (from triangles AEO and AFO) and $BE = CF$ (from triangles OEB and OFC).

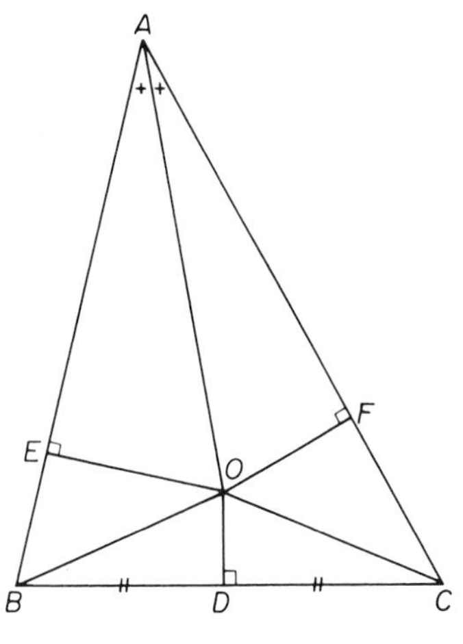

Figure 10.1

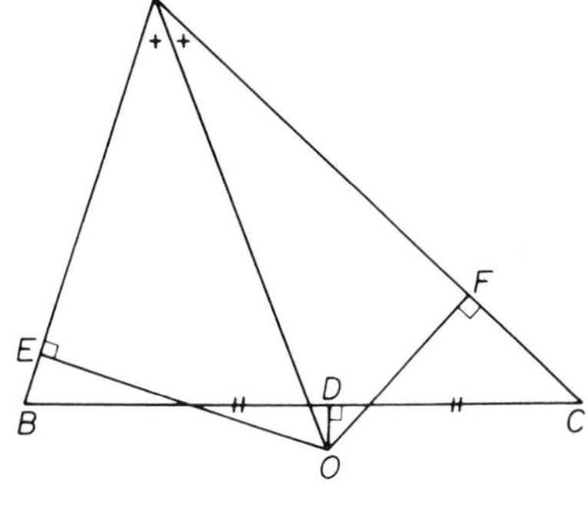

Figure 10.2

10.6. HILBERT'S AXIOMS

About 1900, David Hilbert gave the first complete set of axioms for Euclidean Geometry. Other equivalent sets of axioms have since been discovered.

Hilbert took *points*, *lines*, and *planes* as his undefined objects, and *incidence*, *being in*, *being between*, *congruence*, *being parallel*, and *being continuous* as his undefined relations. His axioms are divided into five types.

I. *Axioms of incidence*, which characterize the relations of *incidence* and *being in*.
II. *Axioms of order*, which characterize the relation of *being between*.
III. *Axioms of congruence*, which characterize the *equality* of line segments and angles.
IV. *Axiom of parallels*, which corresponds to Euclid's axiom V.
V. *Axioms of continuity*, which take care of such things as the existence of line segments larger than a specified segment, and the points of intersection of circles.

The Hilbert assumptions are listed in detail in the following paragraphs; they cast valuable light on the basic foundations of Euclidean geometry, but naturally no one would use all of them explicitly when presenting the subject to elementary students. In particular, Pasch's Axiom illustrates the type of axiom best left to intuition in elementary work.

HILBERT'S AXIOMS

H.1. Undefined Quantities

A class of undefined elements called *points*, denoted by Latin letters $A, B, C, \ldots$.

A class of undefined elements called *lines*, denoted by small Latin letters $a, b, c, \ldots$.

A class of undefined elements called planes, denoted by small Greek letters $\alpha, \beta, \gamma, \ldots$.

Undefined relations: incidence (being incident, lying on); being in; being between; congruence; being parallel; being continuous.

H.2. Axioms of Incidence

Incidence is a symmetric relation between elements of different classes (points, lines, planes) obeying the following axioms.

(H.2.1) Given any two points A, B, there exists a line a lying on (passing through) A and B.

(H.2.2) Given A, B, there exists at most one line a lying on A and B.

(H.2.3) There are at least two points which lie on a given line. There are at least three points which do not lie on a line.

(H.2.4) Whenever A, B, C, do not lie on a line, there exists a plane α such that A, B, C lie on α. Given any α, there exists a point lying on α.

(H.2.5) If A, B, C do not lie on a line, there is at most one α lying on A, B, C.

(H.2.6) If two points on a line a lie in a plane α, then every point lying on a also lies on α.

(H.2.7) If two planes have a point in common, then they have at least one more point in common.

(H.2.8) There are at least four points which do not lie on a plane.

H.3. Axioms of Order

(H.3.1) If B is between A and C, then A, B, C are three different points on a line, and B is between C and A.

(H.3.2) Let A and C be two points and let AC be the line on which A and C lie. Then there exists at least one point B on AC such that C is between A and B.

(H.3.3) Let A, B, C be points on a line; then at most one of them is between the two others.

(H.3.4) (*Pasch's Axiom*) Let A, B, C be three points which are not on a line. Let b be a line in the plane defined by A, B, C such that none of the points A, B, C lies on b. Let b intersect the line AB in a point D between A and B. Then there is either a point X or a point Y on b, where X is between A and C, and Y is between B and C.

H.4. Axioms of Congruence

The axioms of incidence and of order make it possible to define the terms "interval", "side of a line or of a plane", "beam or ray", and "angle".

(H.4.1) Let A and B lie on a. Let A' be on a', which may be different from or incident with a. Then it is always possible to find on a', on either side of A', a point B' such that the interval AB is congruent with $A'B'$, that is, $AB \equiv A'B'$.

(H.4.2) If both $A'B' \equiv AB$ and $A''B'' \equiv AB$, then $A'B' \equiv A''B''$.

(H.4.3) Let AB and BC be two intervals on a which have only point B in common. Let $A'B'$ and $B'C'$ be two intervals on a' (not necessarily different from a) which have only point B' in common. Then it follows from $AB \equiv A'B'$ and $BC \equiv B'C'$ that $AC \equiv A'C'$.

(H.4.4) Let (h, k) be an angle between the rays h and k which lie on the plane α. Let a' be in a plane α', and let a side of a' in α' be given. Let h' be a beam on α' which starts from O'. Then there exists in α' exactly one beam k' starting from O' such that $(h, k) \equiv (h', k')$ and that all inner points of (h', k') lie on the given side of a'. Every angle is congruent to itself.

(H.4.5) If two triangles ABC and $A'B'C'$ satisfy $AB \equiv A'B'$, $AC \equiv A'C'$, $\angle BAC \equiv \angle B'A'C'$, then $\angle ABC \equiv \angle A'B'C'$.

(H.4.5*) In Axiom (H.4.5), add the restriction that $\angle ABC = \angle A'B'C'$ provided that AB and $A'B'$ define the right-hand rays and that AC and $A'C'$ define the left-hand rays of the angles BAC and $B'A'C'$ respectively. Then we also have $\angle ACB \equiv \angle A'C'B'$.

H.5. Axiom of Parallels

Let a be a line, and let A be a point not on a. Let α be the plane determined by a and A. Then there exists precisely one line on α and A which does not intersect a.

H.6. Axioms of Continuity

(H.6.1) (*Archimedean Axiom*) If AB and CD are any intervals, then there exist points $A_1, A_2, \ldots, A_n$ on the line AB such that

$$AA_1 \equiv A_1A_2 \equiv \cdots \equiv A_{n-1}A_n \equiv CD,$$

and B is between A and A_n.

(H.6.2) (*Axiom of Completeness*) The points on a line form a system which can not be extended if Axioms (H.2.1), (H.2.2), (H.3.1) to (H.3.4), (H.4.1) to (H.4.5), and (H.6.1) remain valid.

(H.6.3) (*Axiom of Neighbourhood*) If any interval AB is given, then there exists a triangle such that there is no interval congruent to AB in the interior of this triangle.

10.7. NON-EUCLIDEAN GEOMETRIES

For many centuries attempts were made to prove Euclid's fifth axiom from the others. These attempts all failed. In the nineteenth century, it was shown that such a proof is impossible; an example was given of a consistent geometrical system satisfying the first four axioms but not the fifth. Since then, many other such geometries have been developed.

For historical reasons the name non-Euclidean is reserved for two special geometries:

1. *Hyperbolic Geometry*, which satisfies Euclid's axioms I, II, III, IV, and not V; and
2. *Elliptic Geometry*, which satisfies axioms I, III, and IV, but in which the interpretation of II is modified so as to allow the total length of a line to be finite.

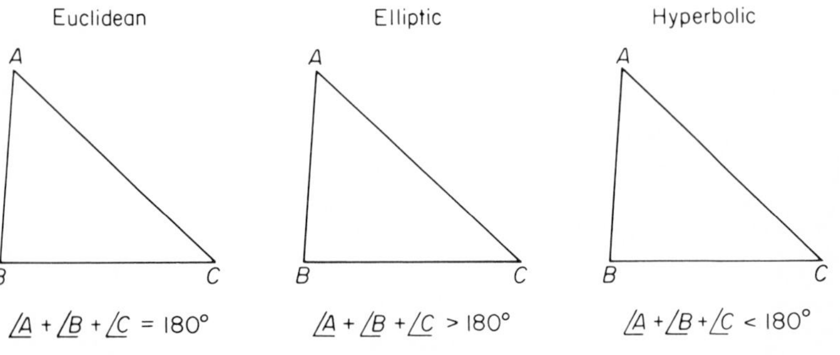

Figure 10.3

These geometries are consistent in the sense that the assumptions underlying them imply no contradictions. Further, it has not been shown conclusively that any one of these does not represent the world of reality.

Many books, which are easily available, have been written on these non-Euclidean geometries; we shall content ourselves with explaining a few theorems which illustrate the differences between the Euclidean, Hyperbolic, and Elliptic geometries. For example, consider the

THEOREM. *In Euclidean (Elliptic, Hyperbolic) geometry, the sum of the angles of a triangle is 180° (greater than 180°, less than 180°).* See Figure 10.3.

THEOREM. *Let P be a point not on the line l. In Euclidean (Elliptic, Hyperbolic) geometry there exists exactly one line (no lines, an infinite number of lines) through P and not meeting l.* See Figure 10.4; in Hyperbolic geometry, the whole pencil of lines between the "right parallel" and "left parallel" fails to meet *l*.

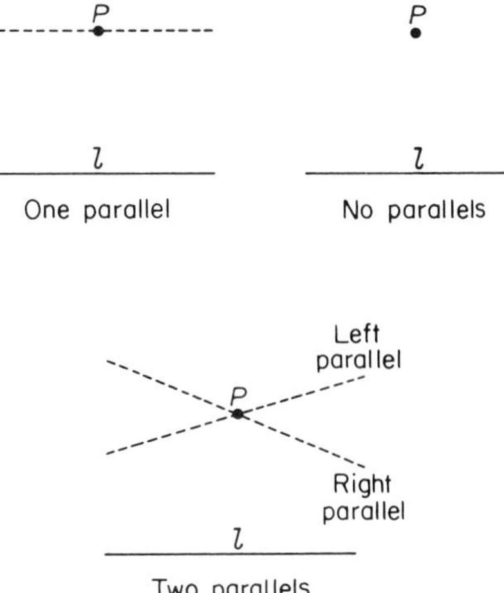

Figure 10.4

Of course, some theorems hold in each of the geometries, since many proofs not involving Euclid's Axiom V are identical in the three geometries. For example, consider (cf. Figure 10.5) the

THEOREM. *The base angles of an isosceles triangle are equal.*

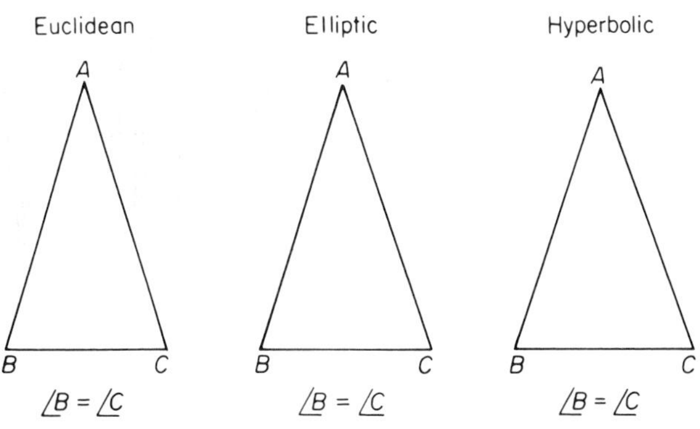

Figure 10.5

10.8. REAL PROJECTIVE GEOMETRY

So far, we have discussed geometries which resemble Euclidean Geometry in many salient features, but differ in those features dependent upon properties of parallelism. We shall now move farther afield to consider geometries which differ much more markedly in their conceptual nature.

In the nineteenth century, attempts were made to find simple geometries not based upon the intuitive properties of measurement. These attempts led to projective geometries, which deal only with points, lines, and their intersection properties, without introducing any metric properties. The main axioms of plane projective geometry are:

A. Every two distinct points lie upon a unique line.

B. Every two distinct lines intersect in a unique point.

The first of these axioms holds in Euclidean geometry; the second does not, since parallel lines exist. However, it is possible to add points and a line to Euclidean geometry so that both axioms are satisfied in the enlarged system. This geometry is called *real plane projective geometry.*

To construct real plane projective geometry, let us start with ordinary analytic Euclidean geometry in which the points are the number pairs (x, y), with x and y arbitrary real numbers, and the lines are the sets of points (x, y) which satisfy an equation of the form $Ax + By + C = 0$, where A and B are not both zero.

Now one of the main principles of mathematics, the principle of *symmetrization*, can be introduced. Instead of x and y, let us write

$$x = \frac{X}{Z}, \qquad y = \frac{Y}{Z} \qquad (Z \neq 0).$$

Then we can say that a Euclidean point is determined by a number triplet (X, Y, Z) with $Z \neq 0$; furthermore, two points or number triplets will be identical if X, Y, and Z are proportional. For example, the triplets $(6, 5, -3)$ and $(-3, -2.5, 1.5)$ are identical, and determine the ordinary point $(-2, -\frac{5}{3})$. Also, a Euclidean line now consists of all number triplets (X, Y, Z) which have $Z \neq 0$ and satisfy the symmetric relation $AX + BY + CZ = 0$, where A and B are not both zero.

Now let us use another mathematical principle, the *principle of generalization.* We enlarge our Euclidean geometry (for the system of triplets is still just our Euclidean system with a different nomenclature) by adding "ideal" points for which Z is zero. Our system then consists of all "points" or triplets (X, Y, Z) where X, Y, and Z are any real numbers, not all zero, and where two triplets (X, Y, Z) and (X_1, Y_1, Z_1) are identified if and only if X, Y, Z are proportional to X_1, Y_1, Z_1; furthermore, we allow $Z = 0$ to represent the equation of a line, that is, our generalized lines consist of all triplets (X, Y, Z) which satisfy the condition $AX + BY + CZ = 0$, where A, B, and C are not all zero.

This enlarged system is called *real plane projective geometry*. It is not hard to verify that axioms A and B are satisfied. Parallel lines of Euclidean geometry do have intersection points in this enlarged system. For example, the lines $x + y = 1, x + y = 2$, become $X + Y = Z, X + Y = 2Z$, and these lines intersect in the ideal point $(-1, 1, 0)$. This case, along with two others, is illustrated in Figure 10.6.

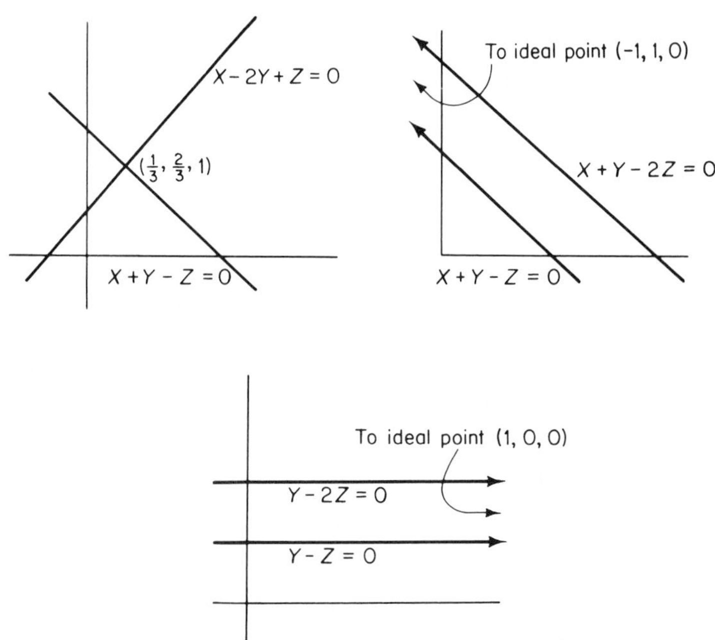

Figure 10.6

It is clear that the theorems of real projective geometry correspond to theorems in Euclidean geometry. For example, let us consider

DESARGUES' THEOREM. Let A, B, C, A', B', C', be any six points such that the lines AA', BB', and CC' are concurrent in a point O. Let D be the point of intersection of the lines BC and $B'C'$, E be the point of intersection of CA and $C'A'$, F the point of intersection of AB and $A'B'$. Then D, E, and F are collinear. (This situation is illustrated in Figure 10.7.)

In Euclidean Geometry, special cases of Desargues' Theorem must be included to allow for the possibility that pairs of lines such as AB and $A'B'$ be parallel. For example, under the same assumptions, if AB is parallel to $A'B'$ and BC is parallel to $B'C'$, then CA is parallel to $C'A'$ (cf. Figure 10.8). The beauty of real projective geometry, as opposed to Euclidean Geometry, is that no such exceptions due to parallelism need be considered, since *every* two lines meet.

We shall conclude this section by illustrating the methods of projective geometry. Very often, problems in ordinary analytic geometry may be simplified algebraically by a judicious choice of coordinate axes. This principle can be extended to projective geometry. Instead of two axes corresponding to $x = 0$ and $y = 0$, we say that there are three coordinate axes in projective geometry, corresponding to $X = 0$, $Y = 0$, and $Z = 0$. These form a *triangle of reference.*

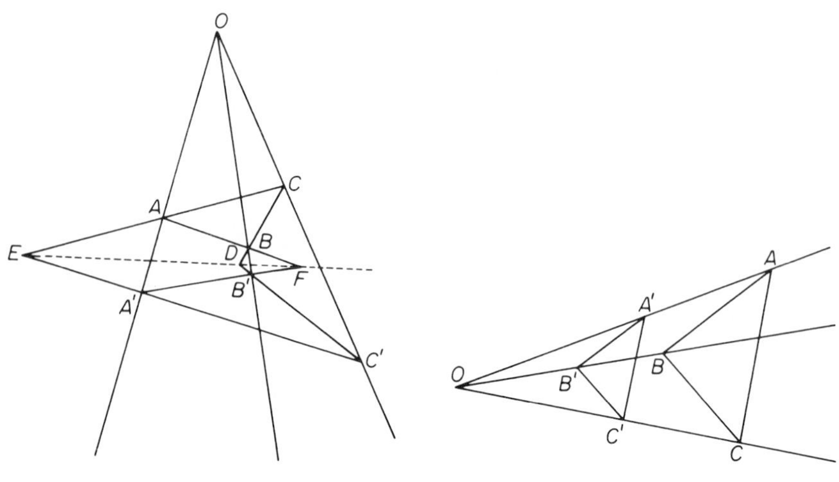

Figure 10.7 **Figure 10.8**

It is not hard to show that the coordinates can be chosen so that *any* specified triangle plays the role of triangle of reference. This corresponds in the familiar case to selecting *any* pair of perpendicular lines through any point as the coordinate axes. In projective geometry, we can make a further simplification. After selecting the triangle of reference, we can select any point, not on a side of the triangle of reference, and assign to it the coordinates (1, 1, 1). This point is called the *unit point.*

Any theorem of Euclidean geometry which does not involve measurements of distances or angles must also be a theorem of real projective geometry. The use of projective coordinates sometimes leads to great simplification. Not only can we make use of symmetry more easily, but any triangle can be taken as the triangle of reference, and any point not on its sides can be taken as the unit point.

To illustrate, let us prove the following theorem analytically.

THEOREM. Points A', B', C', are taken on the sides of triangle ABC so that AA', BB', and CC' are concurrent in a point O. If $B'C'$, $C'A'$, and $A'B'$ meet BC, CA, and AB at D, E, and F respectively, then D, E, and F are collinear.

Let the given triangle ABC be the triangle of reference, and O the unit point, that is, $A = (1, 0, 0)$, $B = (0, 1, 0)$, $C = (0, 0, 1)$; the equations of BC, CA, and AB are $X = 0$, $Y = 0$, and $Z = 0$, respectively. Then AO has equation $Y = Z$, and intersects the line $BC\,(X = 0)$ in the point $(0, 1, 1)$; hence A' has coordinates $(0, 1, 1)$. Similarly, $B' = (1, 0, 1)$ and $C' = (1, 1, 0)$. The line $B'C'$ has equation $X - (Y + Z) = 0$, and intersects $BC\,(X = 0)$ in $(0, 1, -1)$; so $D = (0, 1, -1)$. In exactly the same way, it can be shown that

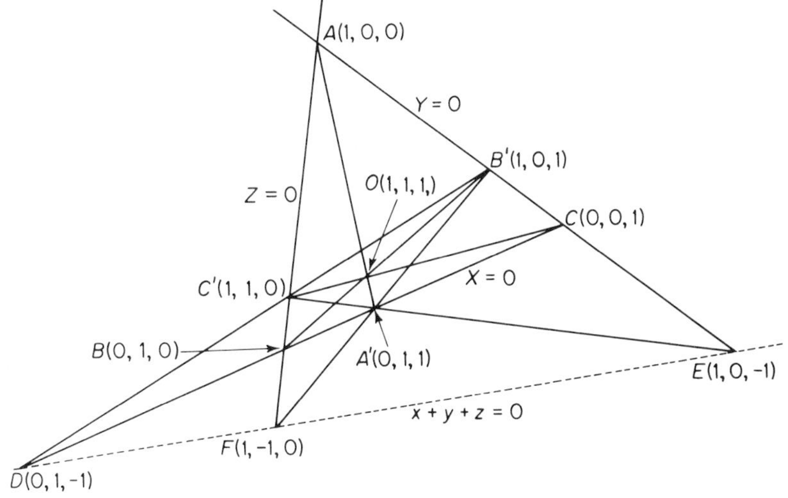

Figure 10.9

$E = (1, 0, -1)$ and $F = (1, -1, 0)$. The coordinates of D, E, and F all satisfy the equation $X + Y + Z = 0$. Thus, D, E, and F are collinear, as was required.

The power of the projective method can be illustrated by trying to prove the preceding theorem using only ordinary analytic geometry. Notice that the theorem is a special case of Desargues' Theorem.

EXERCISES

1. Prove Desargues' Theorem in the general case using the method suggested by the preceding example. (Notice the difficulties that would be encountered using the usual methods of analytic geometry.)

10.9. FINITE PROJECTIVE GEOMETRIES

It is natural to inquire whether other projective geometries exist. In particular, can a projective geometry have only a finite number of points?

This question was not answered until the end of the nineteenth century when Fano constructed the first finite geometry. Since then, an infinite number of finite projective geometries have been constructed.

At this stage, we must again emphasize the fact that "points" and "lines" are undefined elements in geometry. Consequently, we mean by a line simply a *collection of points*. From this general point of view, we may represent the Fano plane in Figure 10.10. There are seven points $F_1, F_2, \ldots, F_7$, and seven lines each containing three points. Six of the lines are represented by ordinary lines. The seventh is *represented* by the circle $F_2F_6F_7$. It is impossible to represent the lines of this geometry entirely by ordinary lines, in the physical plane. Note further that the diagram only *represents* the geometry; "line" $F_1F_2F_4$ contains only three points, and *no others.*

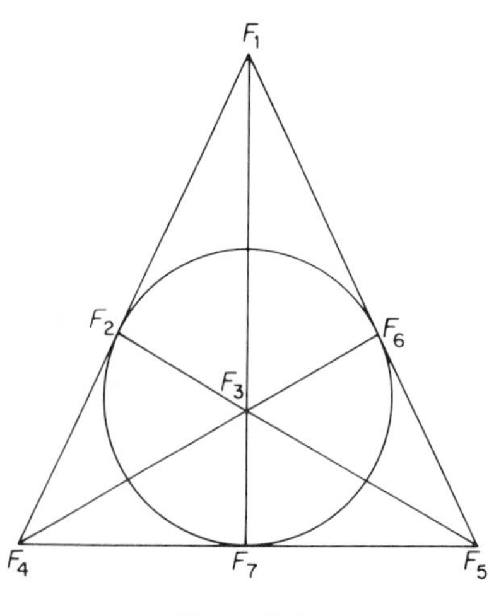

Figure 10.10

Indeed, since points and lines are not defined in geometry, there is no reason why we must use dots and strokes to represent them. We could, for example, let the points be seven firemen $F_1, F_2, \ldots, F_7$, and let the lines be the seven night schedules for a particular week. The Fano geometry would then be the following timetable of night assignments.

Night Schedule

Monday	F_1	F_2	F_4
Tuesday	F_2	F_3	F_5
Wednesday	F_3	F_4	F_6
Thursday	F_4	F_5	F_7
Friday	F_5	F_6	F_1
Saturday	F_6	F_7	F_2
Sunday	F_7	F_1	F_3

Notice that every pair of points (firemen) occurs in exactly one line (schedule), and every pair of lines (schedules) has exactly one point (fireman) in common. Thus the two main axioms of projective geometry are satisfied.

An example of a result which holds in the Fano projective geometry, but not in real projective geometry, is the following

THEOREM. Let A, B, C, D be any four points, no three collinear; let E be the intersection of the lines AB and CD, F the intersection of AC and BD, and G the intersection of AD and BC. Then E, F, and G are collinear.

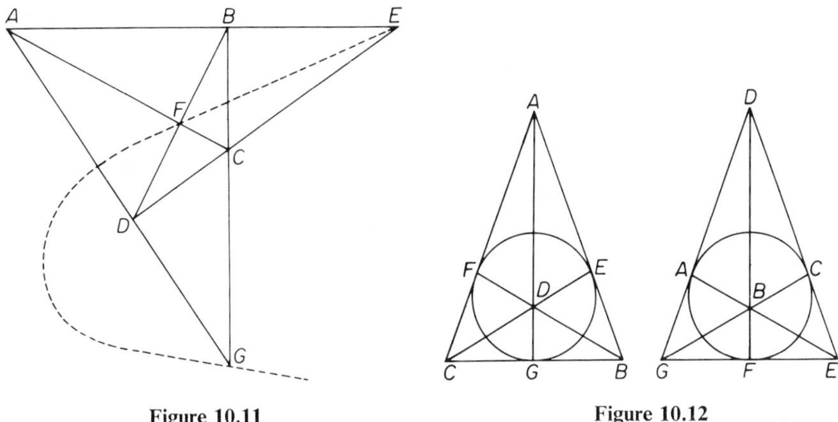

Figure 10.11 **Figure 10.12**

Figure 10.11 shows the situation in real projective geometry; Figure 10.12 illustrates two cases of the truth of the theorem in the Fano geometry. It is clear that E, F, and G can never be collinear in Euclidean geometry.

An example of a theorem true in the Fano geometry and also true in real projective geometry is Desargues' Theorem. This was illustrated in Figure 10.7 for real projective geometry, and is illustrated in Figure 10.13 for the Fano geometry.

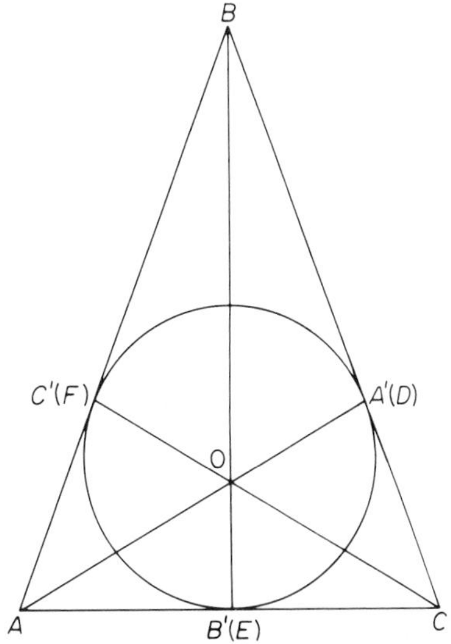

Figure 10.13

Desargues' Theorem holds for an infinite number of projective geometries; recently it has also been shown that Desargues' Theorem fails to hold in an infinite number of projective geometries, the so-called *non-Desarguesian geometries.* It is of interest to note that the main development of these latter geometries has taken place during the last decade.

10.10. ANALYTIC CONSTRUCTION OF THE FANO GEOMETRY

It can be shown that the geometries for which Desargues' Theorem holds can be represented analytically as in the case of real projective geometry. The construction is exactly the same as for real projective geometry with some other "field" used in place of the real numbers. Thus, if F is some field, the projective plane geometry determined by F consists of all triplets

(X, Y, Z) where X, Y, Z are elements of F, not all zero; two triplets (X, Y, Z), and (X_1, Y_1, Z_1) are equal if there is an element α in F so that

$$X_1 = \alpha X, \quad Y_1 = \alpha Y, \quad Z_1 = \alpha Z, (\alpha \neq 0).$$

Finally, the lines of the geometry consist of the collections of points satisfying linear relationships

$$AX + BY + CZ = 0,$$

where A, B, and C are in F, and are not all zero.

The meaning of a field has been already discussed in Chapter 1. We recall that the simplest field contains two numbers 0 and 1 and has the following rules for addition and multiplication.

$$0 + 0 = 0, \quad 1 + 0 = 0 + 1 = 1, \quad 1 + 1 = 0;$$

$$0 \cdot 0 = 0, \quad 1 \cdot 0 = 0 \cdot 1 = 0, \quad 1 \cdot 1 = 1.$$

(The concepts "even" and "odd" have the same arithmetic properties with "even" corresponding to 0 and "odd" to 1.)

The "points" of the corresponding geometry are the triplets (X, Y, Z), with X, Y, and Z selected from the numbers 0 and 1 of this field, and with X, Y, Z, not all zero. Thus, there are exactly seven points, namely,

$$(1, 1, 1), (0, 1, 1), (1, 0, 1), (0, 0, 1), (1, 1, 0), (0, 1, 0), (1, 0, 0).$$

The lines are the sets of these points that satisfy equations of the form $AX + BY + CZ = 0$ with A, B, C, not all zero simultaneously. There are exactly seven lines, namely,

$$X + Y + Z = 0, \quad Y + Z = 0,$$

$$X + Y = 0, \quad Z = 0,$$

$$X + Z = 0, \quad Y = 0, \quad X = 0.$$

It is easy to check that exactly three points lie on each line. For example, the line $X + Y + Z = 0$ contains the three points $(1, 1, 0)$, $(0, 1, 1)$, and $(1, 0, 1)$ and no others.

The geometry constructed in this way is an analytic representation of the Fano geometry. This is easily demonstrated by examining Figure 10.14 where the points of the Fano geometry are given analytically (with co-ordinates and equations). The co-ordinates $(1, 1, 1)$ and $(0, 1, 1)$ can be assigned to two arbitrary points; $(0, 1, 0)$ may be assigned to any point not

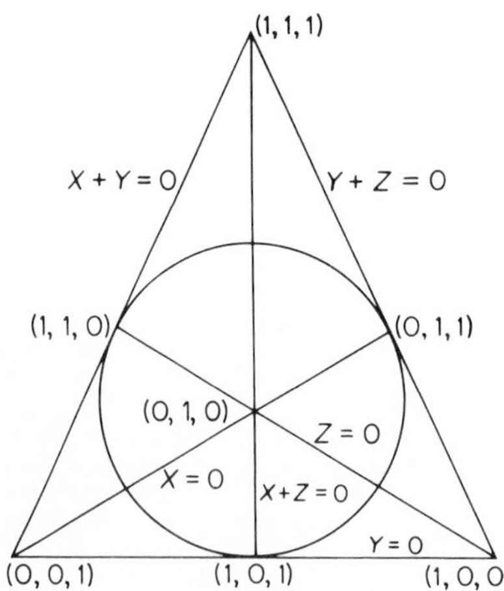

Figure 10.14

on the line determined by (1, 1, 1) and (0, 1, 1). All the other points are then uniquely determined (cf. Exercise 1).

Any other field may be used in exactly the same way to construct a projective geometry analytically in the manner as described above. The problem of constructing all finite non-Desarguesian geometries is one of the outstanding problems in this subject currently being tackled.

EXERCISES

1. Show that there are exactly 168 ways of assigning the coordinates of points in Figure 10.14.
2. Construct a projective geometry of 13 lines and 13 points by using the field consisting of 0, 1, 2 (addition and multiplication being defined modulo 3). Remember that (2, 2, 1) is the same point as (1, 1, 2), etc.
3. Let F be a field containing s elements; find the number of points in the corresponding projective geometry. Find also the number of lines, the number of points on each line, and the number of lines through each point.

EPILOGUE

Some Questions about Modern Mathematics in the Secondary School Curriculum

by Ralph G. Stanton
Kenneth D. Fryer

We should like to conclude this series of essays by raising some questions which are related to current discussions as to the amount of "modern" mathematics which should find a place in the secondary school curriculum. To this end, we have adopted a tabular form.

1. It is well to start any discussion of the effect of "modern" mathematics upon the secondary school curriculum by explaining the background from which one proffers opinions. In North America, the level of mathematics attained by secondary school graduates in one region may vary markedly from the level attained by graduates in another region. The authors of this volume are speaking from experience based on the Ontario Grade XIII curriculum; under this system, all students who take mathematics in University enter with a basic knowledge of Plane Analytic Geometry (the straight line, the circle, the three conic sections), Senior Algebra (this course is equivalent to most so-called courses in "College Algebra", and includes work on functions, the binomial series, permutations and combinations, and

the like), and Trigonometry (the usual work on triangles, the trigonometric functions, analytic trigonometry, and statics). Would it not be desirable that all mathematics students entering college should enter with this background in Analytic Geometry, Algebra, and Trigonometry?

2. Has there been too great a tendency among proponents of modern or "progressive" mathematics to label opponents as reactionary, traditional, and conservative? Would it not be possible to adopt some of the good ideas in "progressive" mathematics without denying that many of the traditional topics and approaches have value?

3. Will changing from a traditional to a "progressive" curriculum really improve the teaching of mathematics? Or is changing the curriculum only one facet of a social problem? Has sufficient thought been given to considerations such as are found in "Second Thoughts on Modernizing the Curriculum" by D. M. Merriell (*American Mathematical Monthly*, January, 1960)? "The possibility of improvement depends on some very complex social questions. It is well known that it is very difficult to change an entrenched curriculum. But the possibility of changing social attitudes and values seems so much more remote that one suspects that the curriculum question has been singled out in order to give the illusion of progress rather than attempting to strike at the real heart of the educational problem .... Nevertheless, now that the machinery for curriculum revision has been set up and the times are propitious, one should be flexible enough to investigate alternatives".

4. Is there a danger of premature emphasis on the axiomatic method? Is this method likely to lead to excesses in the hands of inexperienced teachers? Are some of the proposals for a progressive curriculum confusing the question of what *can* be taught to elementary students with the question of what *should* be taught to elementary students?

5. Does a student's command of either English or mathematics benefit from a very early emphasis on notation? Does "$x \in N$" possess a real advantage over the statement "x is an integer"?

6. Is the phrase "open sentence" more conducive to mathematical understanding than "equation"? Is the progressive phraseology

> "Obtain the solution set made up of all x's such that $x^2 = 100$ and x is contained in the set of integers; that is, obtain
> $$S = \{x \mid x^2 = 100, x \in I\}\text{"}$$
> any real improvement over "Solve the equation $x^2 = 100$"? Should one go even farther and replace the old problem "Solve: $3x + 2y = 4$, $7x - 4y = 6$" by the "new" problem: "Determine the solution set
> $$S = \{(\square, \triangle) \mid 3\square + 2\triangle = 4, 7\square - 4\triangle = 6; \square \in \text{Re}, \triangle \in \text{Re}\}\text{?"}$$

Or should one adopt the point of view put forth by A. M. Gleason (*American Mathematical Monthly*, November, 1961)? "Among the so-called modern approaches to college mathematics are those that put altogether too much emphasis on formal logic and set theory. . . . It does not take very much formal manipulation of nonsense statements or cup and cap signs to convince a bumptious freshman that mathematics is trivial and impractical. He is likely to drop the subject, read a semipopular book, and become a firm believer in the curves-on-pretzels canard. Let us not start any subject unless we can take it far enough to justify the effort."

7. Do some of the "teaching machine" proponents favour more progressive mathematics because it is easy to programme? Beginning with the statement that 0, 1, 2, 3, 4, 5, 6, 7, 8, are whole numbers, one can end up with a statement, *after 89 steps and in one hour* [*Time*, March 24, 1961], to the effect that

$$\text{“}(7) \subset \{1, 3, 5, 7, 9\}\text{” means that } \{7\} \text{ is a subset of } \{1, 3, 4, 7, 9\}.$$

Is such an approach to the statement "Seven is a whole number" likely to develop mathematical ability?

8. Can mathematical facility and manipulation be abandoned in favour of "mathematical concepts"? Or is there an analogy with English, where a knowledge of grammar seems helpful in writing good prose?

The preceding questions are among those which may be raised concerning various aspects of progressive mathematics, and we think it is fitting to close with a plea for close *scrutiny* of new proposals. The progressive point of view has been presented, over the past few years, in great volume; consequently, in this epilogue we have felt it proper to suggest that the traditional approach is not entirely devoid of virtues. Scrutiny is all-important; one should not reject all progressive ideas because some of them appear dubious; similarly, one should not reject traditional approaches because the progressives may wish to eliminate them. There is an old quotation from a very wise teacher which states: "Never believe anything *merely* because it has been told you by me or any other teacher". This quotation should inspire every teacher to scrutinize new "progressive" proposals, but not to blithely and automatically accept every new proposal which is put upon the market merely because it is labelled as being modern, progressive, and a "Good Thing".

Addendum. Three recent articles which will be found especially thought-provoking are:

"On the Mathematics Curriculum of the High School", *American Mathematical Monthly*, 1962, pp. 189–193.

"The Narrow Mathematician", C. B. Allendoerfer, *American Mathematical Monthly*, 1962, pp. 461–469.

"Mathematics Teaching Reforms Assailed as Peril to U.S. Scientific Progress", Morris Kline, *N.Y.U. Alumni News*, October, 1961.

Index

U

V

Z